'Are you a coward, Riva?'

I've told you I never run.'

'What if there are storms in the offing? Will you try and weather them?'

'Storms don't scare me. And I'm not a fair-weather sailor either.' Riva gave a half-smile, remembering what he had said once before.

Richard remembered it too and began to laugh softly. 'I don't believe you are. So, as I said, it's going to be interesting—and I'm a patient man when necessary. It'll be interesting to wait and see what you decide to do. . .'

'Well,' she said, getting her voice back under control, 'I do hope you won't be too disappointed. What *I* decide to do won't be anything *you'll* find worth waiting for.'

He laughed darkly. 'Don't be too sure, Riva. Just don't be too sure. . .'

BRIDE OF RAVENSCROFT

BY

SALLY HEYWOOD

MILLS & BOON LIMITED
ETON HOUSE   18–24 PARADISE ROAD
RICHMOND   SURREY   TW9 1SR

First published in Great Britain 1990
by Mills & Boon Limited

© Sally Heywood 1990

Australian copyright 1990
Philippine copyright 1990
This edition 1990

ISBN 0 263 76712 4

Set in 11 on 12½ pt Linotron Times
01-9006-44999
Typeset in Great Britain by Centracet, Cambridge
Made and printed in Great Britain

CHAPTER ONE

THE beach was a breathtaking silver crescent with a line of perfect surf forming and reforming in patterns of delicate lace at its edge. Apart from the two people sitting on white chairs half in and half out of the water at its far end, it was deserted. A thatched terrace cupped in a hollow on low-lying cliffs indicated the presence of a villa, and woodsmoke from the evening barbecue drifted languidly among the graceful arch of palms in the gardens above.

Riva was almost asleep, senses lulled by the surge and withdrawal of the sea around her feet. From beneath her straw hat she could see her brown legs stretched out in front of her, and if she tilted her head, assuming she wanted to do anything so strenuous, she could bring into view the motionless form of her companion. A wave trailed lace over their tanned feet, then withdrew. There was silence apart from the sound of the surf, the wild cry of a seagull, the distant chatter of parrots in the trees. Minutes ticked by.

Eventually one of the servants switched on some dance music at the house and Riva tapped the bare brown arm next to her own. 'Time for supper.' She sighed.

There was a grunt. 'Sorry, sweetheart, I was asleep. It's heaven here, isn't it?'

Riva didn't reply, but her silence was as eloquent as speech to her companion.

He watched her covertly as she sat for another minute, tilting her straw hat on to the back of her head, letting the last rays of the westering sun gild her sunburned face. Her blonde hair was bleached almost white, contrasting stunningly with the shocking pinks and bright blues of her bikini. A whisper of gold at her neck was her only other adornment.

'Riva,' he touched her lightly on the back of the arm. 'I won't stand in your way. If you really want to leave I'll understand.'

'It seems so ungrateful,' she replied, blue eyes clouded as she gazed away to the horizon. 'It's not as if I have any proper plans. No burning ambitions! Nothing that seems to justify leaving. . .' She turned, pushing her hat right back so that she could look across at the face of the man beside her. It was very dear to her. The once black hair now quite white, the distinguished beard grizzled, the strong lines of the face with its shrewd grey eyes as sombre as her own right now. 'Dad, I'm sorry. I've got to live life for myself.'

'I know, love. I've been expecting this for a long time. You're twenty-two. I've been lucky to have you with me for so long. And Riva——' the hand on her arm tightened a little '——I'm sorry if I've failed you—I know it hasn't been a conventional upbringing, but it was the best I could do. I thought I'd got it right——'

'Dad, if you dare say anything like that I'll—I'll dunk you in the sea!' She tried to smile, but the sorrow of the parting she now knew was inevitable was so strong that she could only make a feeble attempt and her eyes misted for a moment. 'Listen, Dad, you've given me a great life,' she told him urgently. 'I know I've been to umpteen schools since Mum died. But think of all the wonderful places we've lived——'

'Never anywhere for more than three months at a time?'

'OK. So it's that that's finally forcing me to take stock. But think of all the countries I know—not just as a tourist, but as somebody who's lived native, sharing life with the local people——'

'And falling in love with them.' He eyed her solemnly for a moment. 'I know, love. No sooner did you start to feel part of the local scene than I'd uproot you again and move on somewhere else. That last one was the one that hurt, wasn't it?'

Riva laughed softly. 'Dad, if he'd been the right one I would never have come away with you that last time. Truly. You don't have to go all guilt-ridden on me!' She hit him playfully on the arm. 'It would be out of character and totally unconvincing if you did!'

'I'm a selfish devil, is that what you're trying to tell me?' He laughed. 'You know, Riva, perhaps I am. Let it be a lesson to you. You deserve a man who'll put you first. Remember that. Don't go for a father-figure, go for good husband material.'

'Honestly!' She pretended to look shocked. 'I'm not leaving you in order to look for a husband! Heaven forbid! I want to discover life on my own account first. I've been the spoilt daughter of the great Maxwell Hammond, screen writer extraordinary, for far too long. Now I'm going to be plain Riva Hammond, working girl, no privileges and no rewards beyond those I earn myself!'

'I'm going to increase your allowance, of course——'

'No!' Her eyes softened. 'Look, Dad, don't let's quarrel about that at this stage. I told you no when we discussed it before. I really mean it. How can I ever learn to stand on my own two feet if I don't even have the incentive to go out and find a job? No—thanks, and no, thanks. Let me do this my own way.'

'Sweetness, you go for one hundred per cent every time, don't you? All right, try it for three months. I shan't say I told you so if you want to come back. I'll be too damned pleased,' he added feelingly. 'I know I shan't get a PA as good as you. I await the arrival of super-secretary Miss Smithson with honest dread.'

'I'm sure she'll be exactly what you need.'

'Need, perhaps. But want?' He looked unconvinced. 'At least with you around I knew my social life was my own. Now I expect to be preyed on by every woman who gets me in her sights!'

Already he was thinking of himself. Riva was

used to that. For years she had put him first, his every whim having the force of a silent command, and so smoothly had she dovetailed his wishes into the demands of his punishing work schedule that he scarcely knew the extent of her own sacrifice in doing so. And it was true about women. He wasn't being conceited when he spoke like that. Riva was used to that too, to the wiles of the sort of women who regarded Maxwell Hammond, his wealth and his considerable fame on top of that, as an irresistible lure. 'You'll cope!' She got up as the dinner gong resounded from the terrace.

'At least there's the flat in Knightsbridge for you!' Maxwell smiled complacently as he stood up and gave one last lingering look at the sunset. Secretly he thought she'd be back well within three months. Luxury was second nature to her. She wouldn't like roughing it; the glamour of that would soon pall. But it was something she had to get out of her system.

It had been that handsome young devil in Michigan who had put the doubts in her mind, and at a certain age the appeal of a nice little house with the prospect of children was simply too strong to resist. That Riva had resisted and was here now beside him showed that she intuitively knew that playing wifey to an insurance executive, no matter how good-looking, was not for her. She wasn't the stuff of PTA meetings and ballet-class rotas! But she was a chip off the old block—and needed time to prove it for herself.

Looking at her now as she gracefully strode along beside him like a young bronzed Venus, he didn't doubt that as soon as she saw herself in print she would understand how different, how special she really was. All thoughts of burying herself away would disappear. He would help matters along by seeing what he could do about those song lyrics and the short stories of hers as soon as she'd left.

She walked alongside him, hanging on to one of his arms as she used to do when she was a child, her eyes bright now as she planned the next few months. 'Look on me as having an adventure in reverse,' she told him as they reached the terrace. 'Instead of seeking out something strange and unexpected, I'm going to become ordinary at last. No more hobnobbing with the flashy and famous, just a plain, ordinary job with sensible low-key people who'll accept me as I am.'

'A sort of Cinderella in reverse?' His expression was ironic. 'It's an interesting concept, Riva, but what if somebody recognises you as the fairy princess despite the rags and ashes. . .?'

The glittering coach in the shape of her father's white chauffeur-driven Cadillac didn't turn into a pumpkin but into a nippy little hired Fiesta. Riva was quite content with that as she drove purposefully out of London on her first weekend back in England. And the princess in her was hidden underneath a layer of woolly jumpers, thick socks and sensible shoes, the bright blonde hair scraped back neatly into a plait and hidden beneath a headscarf. The tan was noticeable, but without make-up she looked as ordinary as she knew how.

She had spent a day or two surrounded by the job pages of all the newspapers she could lay her hands on and had earmarked several that seemed likely. What she looked for was the security of long-term prospects, and the promise of a large, friendly office, Christmas parties, birthday celebrations—all the things she knew other people took for granted. But while she waited for a response to her letters of application she was going to take a few days off.

Despite all the years of incessant travelling there were one or two places she had never fully explored and she decided she was going to satisfy her curiosity now while she had the chance.

Wryly she admitted to herself that maybe she was staving off the moment when she would definitely have to put down roots. The habit of being on the move was deeply ingrained. It was only to be expected, given the life she'd led so far. The flat seemed like just another stop-over and she hadn't felt it was the sort of place she could regard as even semi-permanent. In fact, she couldn't wait to get out of it, and with no clear idea of where she wanted to go she decided that, with a few days at her disposal, she would follow up a long-cherished dream.

She had been fascinated by the stories her father wove around the place where she had been born and where she had lived as a baby until the wandering of her two restless parents had resumed. Her interest in the little fishing village on the wild Yorkshire coast had been thoroughly aroused. She couldn't stop herself from dreaming about it, about going back one day and then. . . She didn't know what then, but in her secret heart it was the place she called 'home'.

It was a long drive and by the time she turned off the A1 on to the road that drove straight as a die across the North Yorkshire moors she was ready for a cup of tea. She had forgotten the weather. Even though it was supposed to be early summer a howling gale semed to blow through every crevice of the car, and she had had to keep the heater turned full on since joining the B road. It was a grimly beautiful vista, nothing but the curving lines of the moors on all sides, no sign of life but the ubiquitous sheep, contentedly cropping grass, looking like still grey stones in the distance. She stopped for a moment to stretch her legs and immediately three or four sheep clustered round the open door of the car. 'Sorry, chaps,' she told them, surprised to hear the sound of her own voice in the desolate silence, 'I haven't got a crumb left.'

Soon she was leaving the moors and driving along the coast road, the North Sea spread like a wrinkled grey cloth to one side. There could be nothing more different from the turquoise waters that washed the beaches of Jamaica than these ones, she thought, glancing hurriedly down at the black rocks jutting out of the oily grey waters below the cliffs. It made her wonder if she was doing the right thing, coming back. There were surely more hospitable places for a few days' reorientation!

It wasn't as if she remembered the place, she thought as it drew nearer. All it was was the place where her parents had met, the home of her parents' parents, and their parents before them. She was hazy about how far back that took her. It was more than she'd had up till now. But in a funny way she felt it was time to pay homage to these ancestors of hers even though there wasn't a single living one of them left.

I'll check them out, she told herself. And then I'll look for a nice, dull ordinary job, and see what that's like. Taking comfort from the fact that she would be back in London by the end of the week with several interviews in the offing, and if she tired of playing Cinderella among the ashes she could be back at the ball, back playing princess in Jamaica a few days after that, she drove on.

Eventually the car came to a steep incline and below her lay a huddle of cottages clinging to the shore's edge. She parked at the top and got out, standing for a long moment looking down at her destination. So this was journey's end. . . Unsure whether it was safe to take the car any further, she left it at the top and in a few minutes, well-wrapped against the rain now driving down in icy gusts, she walked eagerly down the cobbled street into the village.

* * *

It had taken only a few minutes to find somewhere to stay the night. A shopper in the post office had pointed her down the high street. 'Try number thirty-two,' she suggested. 'Mrs Fry takes in lodgers.' So Riva had stomped off through the rain in her wellingtons and waterproofs and knocked on the door of number thirty-two. The woman who answered had eyed her suspiciously. 'I only do bed and breakfast in the season,' she had begun. 'I don't reckon on starting till Whit.' Then, relenting, she'd said, 'But come on in, duck. You're drenched through. I'll see what I can do for you.'

She had led Riva into a tiny sitting-room with a blazing fire in the grate. 'A single, would it be?' she had asked first.

Riva had nodded, rainwater already trickling down her neck inside the waterproof jacket.

'I've got a nice single room. It looks out on to the bank,' Mrs Fry had told her. 'Come up and have a look at it and see if it suits.'

Riva had taken the room there and then. 'I've left my bag in the car. I'll just walk back and get it.' She let herself out and Mrs Fry was already putting on the kettle for her return.

As she trudged back up the bank she had a look in the shop windows. There was a general store of some sort, and a post office and a baker's. Then there was a café, boarded up now, and next to that—she peered closer—some sort of water-sports shop. Then a piece of paper caught her eye. 'Assistant urgently required. Apply within.' She was about to turn away when she felt a sudden twinge as if something had pulled her back. She felt her head turn to read the roughly printed notice once again.

Then a smile started up inside. It was tailor-made, wasn't it? What could be more ordinary than working in this back-of-beyond place? It would give her an excuse to get to know the village really well. She could wallow in fantasies about coming home to her roots to her heart's content for a while! Three months should just about cure her—she stopped. It was the three-month syndrome again. If she didn't watch it she would be just like Dad, squeezing a place of its novelty value, then moving on to somewhere new.

Frowning, she turned away. It was a mad idea anyway. Not at all the sort of place she wanted to work. She was after a job with a nice, big, well-established organisation. Not a one-man band like her father's.

She had only gone a pace or two when she looked up with a start. A man had come charging out of the shop and was looking up and down the street with a perplexed expression on his face. When he saw Riva he scowled. 'Did you push that bell?'

'What?'

'The shop bell?' he repeated. 'Somebody just rang it.'

'I—oh. . .' Riva blushed as she realised she had been leaning against the door-frame without thinking. 'It must have been me. I was just reading your notice,' she admitted, and before she could

go on he took her by the arm and propelled her
into the entrance of the shop.

'Thank heavens for that. Can you start right
away? I'd given up on finding anybody. It's the
wrong time of year, of course. All the students
are still in college and anybody with any sense
works for the rainwear factory in town. No pen-
sion when you work for me!' He laughed easily
then turned to peer into her face. 'You from
round here, then? Haven't seen you before.'

'No. I'm—well, yes, sort of. . .actually.'

'And you want a little job to tide you over?
Don't worry, I wouldn't expect anybody permanent,' he told her hastily. 'I might be out of a job
myself six months from now! Still, that's life. Now
then, do you type?'

She nodded before she could stop herself.

'Great. It's all dead easy, then. Nothing to it.
You don't have to answer a lot of technical
questions. If anybody gets too scientific refer them
to me. Hours are a bit erratic—if we're all still
here when the holiday season starts they could be
fairly long. Will that bother you?'

'Look, I——' Riva stopped. There was something appealing about the way he assumed she was
looking for a job like this. He had short dark hair,
the damp giving it a slight curl so that it looked
look like the damp fur of some cuddly animal, a
pair of bright blue eyes, bringing his whole face
alive, and his enthusiasm was irresistible. But it
was obviously no good. She was a potential personal assitant to some high-powered executive.

She had a flat in Knightsbridge. She looked over his shoulder at the little shop.

'I've never worked in a shop before,' she told him frankly. 'I wouldn't know where to begin.'

'It's not all shop work,' he countered. 'That's half the trouble. I must have somebody who can handle the office side by themselves, talk to customers, get the files in order. You're not a fool, are you?' He stopped as if giving her chance to decide.

She shook her head. 'Only in some things,' she came back.

He laughed, a rich, attractive sound. 'That's it, then. So long as you give the right change and make sure they sign the back of the cheques, you'll be running the shop with one hand tied behind your back,' he paused, 'and maybe set those blue eyes of yours to work, eh?'

'Sorry?'

'Selling,' he replied succinctly. 'These new designs are simply walking out, but a bit of soft-sell when I meet the big retailers is always useful.' He stopped suddenly. 'You won't want paying too much, will you?'

'Just the going rate. I mean—look here, I haven't said I'll take the job. I was only looking in the window. The notice just happened to catch my eye.'

His face fell. One hand ran rapidly through the dark hair. 'Hell, I've been working thirty-six hours without a break. Then you come along and you seem just perfect.' He turned away and Riva bit her lip at the sudden sag in the broad shoulders.

'The trouble is,' she began uncertainly, 'I've only just arrived. I'm staying in a bed and breakfast place down the high street, Mrs Fry's,' she added, as if that would make her rejection more acceptable. 'She's just put the kettle on,' she added lamely.

'If it's accommodation worrying you, it's no problem at this time of year,' he swung back. 'There's a holiday cottage down by the staithe that would do nicely for a girl like you. Shall I point it out to you?'

'But——'

'I'm sorry. I'm not thinking properly. You're probably looking for something more exciting. And what this job is can be summed up in one word—dull! Long hours, poor pay, dingy surroundings. And ideally I want somebody nice and sensible who can bring a bit of stability into our lives!' He shrugged disarmingly. 'Not the sort of thing a girl like you would want!'

Riva stared at him before speaking. 'Maybe you could give me time to think it over?' she said slowly. 'Will you be here for the rest of the afternoon?'

'And the night too,' he replied cheerfully. 'Just lean on the bell if you change your mind.' With a little shrug that told her he thought she was merely letting him down gently, he disappeared inside the shop, closing the door firmly between them and vanishing into a back room.

It was still raining. For a minute or two Riva had forgotten how uncomfortable she felt. Now she set off again up the hill, conscious of the rain inside the collar of her coat.

'It is stupid,' she told herself as she lugged her bag back down the hill to Mrs Fry's. 'Just because he said he wants somebody to bring some stability. . .' She noticed there was a light on at the back of the shop. It was still raining. The cobbled street looked like a picture postcard—of the sort the holiday trade would suppress.

Mrs Fry bustled around when she came back, making sure she changed out of her wet things and calling out to Garry, a lanky fourteen-year-old, to take Riva's bag upstairs.

'Now then, love, you try a piece of my home-made curd tart,' she said as she settled her ample form in the chair opposite.

Riva leaned back. It was just the sort of room she'd imagined her granny might have had—pot animals on the mantelshelf, net curtains, a rag rug with a purring black cat on it in front of the fire. Suddenly she felt like staying longer than the few days she'd planned and she wondered about the cottage the man in the shop had mentioned. It might be fun to stay a little longer. There was no urgency about a job, not for the money sake of it anyway.

'I met a man at the water-sports shop,' she began. 'He was looking for an assistant.'

Mrs Fry chuckled. 'Dark, was he, or fair?'

'Dark.'

'That would be the elder of the Palmer lads. Richard. Not so much a lad now, but he's still the devil he was when he was ten. Always into somethng. . .I wondered what had kept you.'

'Of course, I'm not really looking for a job,' she went on, 'but he mentioned a cottage that might be to let. I think I've fallen in love with this place a little bit,' she explained. 'It might be nice to stay longer than planned.'

'You'd be snug at Sea View. I expect that's where he means. Been done out very nicely for a holiday cottage considering. It's even got central heating, so they say. You'd get it cheap just now.'

'He said he'd point it out to me.' She looked at the grandfather clock in the corner.

'Go over and see it while it's still light, then,' suggested Mrs Fry. 'No time like the present. Not that I'm pushing you out of course, love, but I hadn't planned on taking anybody in just yet till I'd redecorated that room you're in. You're all right there for a night or two, of course,' she added hastily.

'It was sweet of you to take me in. But I would like to stay a little longer.'

Half an hour later she was leaning on the bell to the shop again, this time deliberately, and she heard it ring inside, bringing a door deep within flying open. A dark shape hulked against the light. Then once again she was looking into Richard Palmer's bright eyes. They swept her face at once, obviously trying to read her decision before she spoke.

'You'll give it a try?' He pulled her inside. 'You angel, come in out of that damned rain.' He let her wrist drop and swivelled abruptly. 'Want a drink?' he threw over his shoulder. 'Tea—oh, no,' he turned with a flash of white teeth, 'I forgot. You've just had one of Ma Fry's specials. Her curd tart is out of this world, I remember. Well, in that case I can offer you a gin and tonic, whisky—no soda—or——' he frowned and gave her a narrowed glance '—you're not the beer and cider type, are you?'

'Richard, do you never wait for an answer?' She was laughing now. He was sweet. And he still hadn't looked at her the way men always did. Usually it was the first thing they did. After that their reaction was predictable. Being Maxwell Hammond's daughter had always added to her allure, she suspected. It was a relief to know that, whatever Richard Palmer thought of her, it would be coloured only by what he saw before him.

He looked suddenly serious. 'Sorry, you have the advantage over me. Lord knows what else she's been telling you—your name?' He held out a hand.

'Riva Hammond,' she told him, wondering if there would be any reaction. There wasn't. She took his hand.

'Pleased to welcome you aboard, Riva,' he said seriously as he gripped it in his own. 'You look like an angel and I know you're going to be one.'

He released her hand and turned abruptly. 'You can see what a mess everything's in.' He gestured to the piles of correspondence littering the desk and ranged in rows on the floor against one wall. Opening a filing cabinet he took out two glasses and a bottle of Scotch. 'It's malt,' he said, 'so you won't mind it neat.'

'Do you always make assumptions?' she asked, taking the proffered glass nevertheless.

'I do. It's my way. Sorry about that. I'm told I've got other major character defects too, but I can't quite recall what they are at the moment. No doubt you'll refresh my memory before long!' Though he smiled there was a note of bitter humour in his voice, but he was already going on, showing her where she would be working, opening cupboards and drawers and riffling through piles of brochures that lay neatly stacked on a chair.

'This has to go out to over four hundred retail outlets in the next week. It's been sitting there fresh from the printers for two days. It's a straight-forward job—addresses in here.' He held up a blue hard-backed exercise book. 'That could be your first job tomorrow morning.'

Feeling that she should be gasping for breath, Riva looked round the untidy little room. It was obviously meant to be an office. It couldn't have been more ordinary. She turned to him with a smile. 'Is eight-thirty too early,' she paused, 'or not early enough?'

He chuckled. 'I'll give you a key and you can

come in whenever you like. One of us is sure to be here.'

'Us?'

'My kid brother, Ronnie. He's the guy on the sewing-machine.'

'Sorry?'

'I haven't really explained what we do here, have I? As well as selling sailboards and general tackle for the summer visitors, we design water-sports gear—clothing, that is, not the sailboards, there's too much competition from the big high-tech companies for that. But there's a gap in the market for really good, interesting wet suits, harness and so on. All you need are a few ideas and an industrial sewing-machine—oh, and a bit of organisation. And that's where you come in!'

'I see.' Riva couldn't help smiling again. It was crazy. There was something so infectious about Richard Palmer's enthusiasm that she was being swept along by it. 'It's going to be fun working for you,' she said, raising her glass. 'Here's to it!'

'Good.' He was brisk and obviously had things he wanted to get on with, so she was hesitant when she broached the question of the cottage for rent.

He banged a hand on to his forehead. 'Good girl. Nearly forgot. Hang on a minute, I'll give the owner a bell. He lives in Durham, but the key's with the lady living next door.' He rummaged beneath a pile of box files and came up with a phone book. In a moment he was chatting amiably on the phone to someone at the other end and after a few minutes he put the phone down and turned to her with a smile. 'He's amenable if you are.' Then he named a rent that seemed ludicrously low to Riva.

'I guess I can manage that,' she told him carefully.

He came towards her, shrugging on a waterproof jacket grabbed from the back of a chair. The light was fading rapidly now, slanting across the room in a haze of mauves and pinks. He stood looking down at her for a minute and there was a sudden change in his expression, telling her he had looked at her, really looked, for the first time. 'Yes, well. . .' He seemed unexpectedly lost for words and Riva wondered what astonishing thought had entered his head to stem the flow.

He gripped her by the upper arm and turned her towards the door. 'Let's go. It's nearly dark and the electricity won't be on in Sea View.' He swung back to one of the drawers in the wooden desk, coming back with a torch almost at once. His expression was matter-of-fact again, and she wondered if she'd imagined that brief change that had painted something else over the weatherstained features.

But he was already leading her outside and locking up the shop door. It was still raining.

She felt his eyes flicker over her face. 'You can play house for a few minutes while we're down there,' he told her. 'That is, if I manage to get the lights switched on. Then I can look in on my wife.'

CHAPTER TWO

SEA VIEW was exactly what Riva had expected
from its name. A two-up and two-down grey stone
cottage with a pantile roof straight out of a child's
story-book and built a few yards from the harbour, it was done out inside in nondescript blues
and creams with predictable cottage-style furni-
ture and pots of geraniums in the hearth. She fell
in love with it at once.

'It's hell here in winter when the sea gets up,'
Richard told her, looking round, obviously unim-
pressed by the feminine floweriness of it all.
'That's why none of us wants to live in it. But for
summer weekends it's ideal. I wouldn't mind
living here myself then. The sunsets are really
something, if you're into sunsets.' He went to the
sitting-room window and gazed out across the
staithe to the sea that was lying tamely at the foot
of the stone steps with a boat or two rocking
gently in its arms.

'I can't believe that sea gets up to much,' she
said, coming to stand beside him.

'Don't be deceived. It's a treacherous lady,' he
told her, turning to give her a sudden dazzle of
bright eyes. She saw they were almost green just
now, a sea colour, brightening to blue as he
smiled, changeable in the light. They slid over her

before he turned abruptly and went to the door. 'You're staying here, then, while I see Linda?'

Guessing that this was the wife he had alluded to earlier, she nodded. 'I'll have another look round. But I like it, Richard. It's heavenly.'

'No accounting for taste. Still, it'll be easy to keep up and it's about the right size for one. I won't be a minute.'

She went to the window and watched him cross the staithe to a row of cottages further down. He went right along to the end one then disappeared through a yellow door. So that's where he lives, she pondered. No need for him to be so disparaging about Sea View then, was there?

She had already decided which of the two bedrooms she would sleep in by the time he returned. He was looking pale and hardly spoke on the way back up to the shop. When they reached the door he said, 'I've got to get on now, so I'll say goodbye. See you tomorrow!' He left at once, nodding briefly through the shop window as he locked the door between them.

Riva returned to Mrs Fry's. She felt a vague disquiet, but put it down to the speed with which everything seemed to have been settled.

To her surprise she found it extremely easy to slot into a niche with SeaGear Designs, as Richard and Ronnie called their small company. It wasn't what she had left Jamaica for, but it would be fun for a few weeks, and she could see how useful she was going to be, for it wasn't much different from the work she'd been doing for years for her father—organising the filing, dealing with correspondence, phone calls, appointments. Its turnover was higher than she'd expected, going by the look of the shop, though still small when she learned that it had to support Richard and his wife and child and Ronnie and his expensive hobby of stock-car racing.

After she'd been there a few days she felt as if she was part of the team. The two brothers good-naturedly grumbled at each other in front of Riva, treating her like part of the family. When she heard them in the middle of a particularly vitriolic row that morning she noticed how they only paused long enough to see who was coming in before carrying on where they'd left off.

She smiled to herself. It was a new experience, being part of a family, even if it was really only a pretence, part and parcel of a family-run business.

This morning's argument was about money. As always, she thought. Richard was telling Ronnie in no uncertain terms that he didn't intend to work all hours merely to keep him in spare parts for his two cars. 'The profit has to go back into the business. It's too soon to start syphoning it off!' His face was black as thunder this morning.

Ronnie, a fair-haired boy in his teens, gave Riva a wink. 'These old men,' he muttered in a tone deliberately audible to his elder brother, 'they forget what it's like to be young.'

'It's marriage,' replied Riva, joining in. 'It's an expensive business and he obviously stands as a warning to us all!' She gave Richard a teasing smile, but instead of the glitter of humour in the bright eyes he returned her look with a black scowl and moved away.

'Touchy subject, Riva.' Ronnie punched her lightly on the arm. 'I thought you'd guessed that already.'

'Just shut up, Ronnie, and get some work done now you've bothered to show up.' Richard loomed over the hapless Ronnie and Riva suddenly realised how formidable Richard could be. Underneath that jokey, easygoing manner was a fist of steel. Ronnie obviously thought so too, because he gave a small shrug and began to get his things ready for work. It was another bone of contention that Ronnie's weekends were longer than Richard thought they should be. Before he went out Riva gave him a sympathetic look. Richard was behaving like a bear with a sore head. In the four or five days she'd been working for him she'd never known him as touchy as this.

He was standing in the middle of the office now, running a hand through his hair and looking round with a distracted expression.

'What about a cup of coffee, Richard?' She had already taken off her coat and was arranging her morning's work on the now tidy desk.

'Would you?' He gave her a grateful look. 'You're really making a difference to this place. We'll soon have our heads above water.' He went through into the workroom and Ronnie gave her a little thumbs-up sign as he followed him. She heard them discussing the production of a new line in sailboard harness through the open door with no sign of their previous animosity. Orders seemed to be coming in every day and she wondered if they realised they'd have to take on another machinist soon. It would mean buying another sewing-machine. A big outlay for them at this stage, she imagined.

She smiled to herself. It was amazing how easy it was to get caught up in things. She already felt responsible for the way things were being run.

Richard came back in when he heard the kettle. 'I suppose I'd better take one through to him.' The sound of Ronnie's sewing-machine was whirring away in the next room.

'He does very well, you know, Richard. It's not the sort of job a young lad like him would naturally take to.'

Richard frowned. 'I suppose you think I'm hard on him.' He shrugged. 'Maybe I am. Maybe not.' His eyes were dark today, almost black.

'If it's anything you want to talk about—what I mean is, you can talk to me and know it won't go any further,' she told him. There was obviously something very much on his mind.

He drew his lips back in a humourless smile. 'That's a luxury round here, believe me. Say that and mean it and you'll be worth your weight in gold.'

'I do mean it.'

He stood looking down at her for a moment. 'Yes,' he said slowly, 'I suppose you do.' He gave her another smile that didn't reach his eyes. 'In Turkey to establish a bride price they weigh the poor unfortunate then balance her up in gold.' His jaw tightened. 'Riva, have you done anything but work since you arrived here?' he asked abruptly changing the subject.

She shook her head. 'It seems to be catching—why?'

'Maybe a day off is in order. I've got to go up to Middlesbrough tomorrow to see a buyer. Come with me.'

He phrased it in such a way that she couldn't tell whether it was an order or a request. 'That should be interestng,' she replied in neutral tones. 'I've never been there.'

'Where have you been?' He had just been about to turn away, but swung back, interest showing on his face, but she shook her head.

'Nowhere special,' she hedged, suddenly finding the letter she had in her hand an object of fascination. She had known it had to come, but they had been so busy ever since she'd set foot in the place that she thought the initial curiosity her arrival had created had died a natural death. She should have realised questions would eventually be asked. She had parried Mrs Fry's natural curiosity with a few vague remarks about living in London. It wasn't untrue, but it didn't give away too much of the truth either.

Richard was still looking down at her as if waiting for her to go on.

'This letter——' she asked, holding one out at

random '—shall I add anything about the new brochure?' It was a decision she could make herself, but it served to side-track him sufficiently for the matter of her private life to be dropped. She was only putting the matter on hold, she knew that, for she could tell he was beginning to wonder about her. Well, she thought as he went back into the other room with a backward glance, his curiosity was reciprocated. Apart from the fact that he had a wife called Linda and a son called Tom, she didn't know much else about him. Not even how old he was or what he'd done before setting up SeaGear. If he started questioning her he would find the tables well and truly turned.

The sky was pale eggshell when they set off next morning and, sitting beside him as he drove along the coast road, with the sea itself transformed into a glittering wash of blue, Riva suddenly felt like a child on a school outing. They wound the windows down so that the wind ruffled their hair and she tuned the radio to a music programme then settled back to enjoy the ride. He was a good driver and although the car had seen better days the smooth sound of the engine showed that Ronnie had been let loose on it. It was still a far cry from her father's Cadillac. With a little shock she realised she had scarcely given him a thought over the last few days.

'You've really been keeping me busy, Richard.'

'I'm sorry. Are you getting fed up already?' He shot her a quick glance.

'No, I am not!' she reproved. 'I've got more staying power than that!'

He laughed. 'I hope so. You've made a fantastic difference around the place. I couldn't have found anybody better if I'd invented them myself!'

His words made Riva go quiet. Working for her father, she had often had the feeling she had been tailor-made at birth to fit in with his lifestyle. The whole point of getting away had been to find herself. Now she was slipping into a similar role playing nursemaid to Richard Palmer—at least, she would be if she didn't watch it.

'All right?' He glanced quickly down, puzzled by her sudden silence.

'Sorry, just thinking,' she muttered, looking out of the window. As if to confirm her misgivings, Richard said, 'This meeting is pretty important to me—to the firm, that is. It could be the making of SeaGear. The chap we're going to see happens to own a score of sports shops up and down the country. If we can secure an order with him we'll be sitting pretty. I hope you'll do your best to charm the orders from him, Riva.'

Ignoring that, she asked, 'But how can you cope with any more orders, Richard? Poor Ronnie is working his fingers to the bone as it is.'

'Don't worry about that. I've already looked into the possibility of opening a small workshop drawing on the local workforce. There's a lot of unemployed semi-skilled labour available in and around the villages.'

'And capital?'

He shot her an amused look. 'Young, enthusiastic bank manager?'

'OK.' She laughed. 'I wasn't implying you didn't know what you were doing.'

'No?' He chuckled softly. 'Little things mean a lot, Riva, and sometimes you say something, or look in a certain way that hints at so much more than what you let anybody see. I don't suppose direct questioning will satisfy my curiosity, will it?'

She opened her blue eyes wide. 'Mr Palmer, are you suggesting I have a murky past?'

He reached out to grip her hand. 'That would add a little spice to life, wouldn't it?'

'You don't have time for spice. You're too busy on your way to your first million.'

Richard seemed content to leave the matter there, concentrating on the switchback roads that lay ahead, and telling her about the plans he had for the future.

They reached the headquarters of Northern Sports in good time for their appointment. It was a detached Victorian mansion in the town's commercial quarter, converted, rather unfortunately in Riva's opinion, into a functional suite of offices for the chairman, his staff and the sales force. A plump secretary came bustling out to greet them and when she set eyes on Richard she stopped, seemed to gulp, then carried on with what she'd been instructed to say without once taking her eyes off him. Feeling somewhat invisible, Riva resigned herself to her usual role and did what she could to think herself into the part of Richard Palmer's assistant.

When the boss invited them into his office, she heard Richard introduce her as such and she grinned to herself. Only last week she had been lying on a beach in an expensive resort in Jamaica. It was positively unreal to be here talking quotas of wet suits! But a look at Richard's shrewd adversary made her realise it was more than a game. He was one of those self-made men who were as hard as nails when it came to doing business. When he accidentally caught her eye she glittered back at him and was pleased to see him falter for a moment. Richard moved in smoothly with his terms and in a surprisingly short time the deal was clinched.

Sneaking a glance at Richard's face as he sat back while Mr Hargraves buzzed for his secretary, she saw how impassive he seemed. His eyes were like blue ice. But she knew that underneath the courteous smile on his lips he was dancing with joy.

Ashamed of the way she had been silently scoffing at the whole set-up, she rose to her feet when the secretary came in and offered to go with her to photocopy the documents the men required to settle things. Outside in the corridor the girl turned to Riva at once.

'Isn't he gorgeous?' she exclaimed. 'I've never seen such a smashing hunk of male outside the movies. What's he like to work for?'

'Slave-driver,' replied Riva succinctly. 'But I've

only been with him five days. With luck he'll slow down.'

'I'd work round the clock for a guy like that. Lucky you. If you ever think of moving on, let me know!'

Riva giggled. 'I might just do that. I don't intend to stay——' She bit her lip. 'I mean, I guess I'll be moving on some day,' she added lamely. As she stood guard over the photocopier she was thoughtful. The question of how long she remained at SeaGear hadn't come up. Perhaps it was best to leave it like that. Richard himself had told her the first time they met that he wasn't looking for anybody permanent. That had been before an order like this one with Northern Sports had been secured. It was something that might make a difference.

She let Mr Hargraves' secretary bring the copies of the contract back into the office so she could get another glimpse of Richard. It was true, she realised in surprise, following the girl's glance. He was rather dishy. Her senses must have become somewhat jaded with always being around movie stars since as far back as she could remember.

But Richard wasn't a movie star; he was the real thing. His looks weren't the kind bred and nurtured in a gym for the benefit of the market place. He was all tough, masculine command, weather-tanned, with the broad muscular shoulders of a man used to real physical exertion. He moved easily, with an athlete's compact grace, because his life demanded it, not to impress some camera-eye, and looking at him now she guessed that underneath the conventional dark suit, sitting a little awkwardly on him as if he wasn't used to wearing it, he would be all hard muscle.

Then his eyes, his blue-chip eyes, focused on her, sweeping over and through her as if reading off her thoughts as she demurely took her place a little to one side of Mr Hargaves' imposing executive desk. She lowered her own eyes, wondering just what thought had flashed into his mind at that moment.

They got outside half an hour later, and when they were safely out of sight at the back of the building in the car park Richard gripped her by the arm and swung her to face him. 'That was one easy ride!' he exclaimed against the side of her head. 'Without you he'd have driven a much harder bargain. Thank you, Riva. I'll be offering you a directorship at this rate.' He was joking, but there was a look in the depths of his eyes that was completely serious. As if he knew he might be giving away too much, he added, 'Early days though. We have to weather a few storms first, don't we?'

'Do we?' She looked wary, pulling away as she became self-conscious about the unexpected way her body was reacting to his touch.

'A company should be like the crew of a ship. Some people are fair-weather sailors and you would never put out in a Force Ten with them on board.'

'I see.' She went round to her own side of the

car, feeling a sense of relief with the bulk of it safely between them. She felt both hot and cold, alive and unexpectedly jumpy. It was the novelty, of course. His hard man's body was enough to set alight the most unresponsive female, crushing up briefly against hers like that with no warning, and she hadn't been in such proximity to an attractive male of her own generation for weeks!

She shook her head and tried to avoid his glance. 'So you think I'm a fair-weather sailor, do you?' she challenged, trying to keep her tone light.

He didn't reply, but, holding the keys to the car in one hand, instead gave her a burning look across the roof of the car, blue eyes licking over her like flame until she was compelled to drop her gaze and rattle at the handle of the door as if eager to be let in.

'I want to get back to the office as soon as possible to put a few calls through now it's all systems go,' he told her as he headed the car through the town-centre traffic. 'But we'll stop off somewhere for a bite to eat.'

A statement of intent, she thought wryly. It was his style. No 'Would you like to. . .?' or 'Shall we. . .?', merely 'we'll do this. . .we'll do that.'

After about half an hour he pulled into the yard of a coaching inn and ushered her into the lounge. It was quaint with oak beams, copper warming pans, artful arrangements of dried flowers and a delicious smell of home cooking that immediately cancelled out the feeling that it was just a designer façade for a film about merrie England.

As she took her seat on an oak settle by the fire she couldn't help trying to explain. 'It's not real.' She looked round. 'I mean, it is, and it's that that's not real! I'd forgotten what the north of England was like.' She bit her lip. This would be the opening he was waiting for and she'd handed it to him on a plate. But instead of following it up he merely flexed his shoulders, gazing round the room as if he wasn't really seeing it.

It made her acutely aware of the vast differences that separated them. He wouldn't know what she was talking about. He had probably never left the area. Despite his shrewd business brain his horizons would be limited to the parish pump. His lordly self-confidence no doubt came from a feeling of being a big fish—but the pool was little more than a puddle in reality. Even so, when his hand skimmed hers as he handed her a gin and tonic she couldn't conceal a tremor at the contact.

His eyes flickered with electric vitality over her face. 'Nervous? But it's all over now,' he murmured. She found herself looking away in confusion, and before she could think of anything to say he raised his glass. 'Congratulations to us!' he said with a flash of white teeth. 'May all our ventures prosper!'

She swallowed, then gave him a teasing glance. 'I'm not sure we're allowed to toast ourselves, but why not? Good luck, Richard.'

'That's not what I said.' His eyes lazed over her face. There was a silence lasting the length of a heartbeat before he broke it with the question she had been waiting for. His voice was husky. 'So now what, Miss Hammond? Isn't it time you filled in a few blanks for me? Like where you've actually sprung from and what you're really doing up here in this backwater of ours?'

She opened her eyes wide. 'I haven't done anything very much, really. Just this and that.' She shrugged, hoping he would be fobbed off, but he leaned back with a small smile on his lips.

'And where in general have you been doing "this and that"—in the south?'

She nodded. It was true, even if a little further south than he probably envisaged! 'I've got a flat in London. My father's place actually, but he's away a lot so it's virtually my own.'

'So why Scarswick? Why fetch up here?'

'No reason, really. It seemed like a good idea at the time! Dad used to be from around here, though he hasn't been back for twenty years or so. I thought it might be worth a visit. It's a nice place,' she defended suddenly.

'It can be.' He looked in two minds. 'I'm a native. I have mixed feelings.'

'Have you always lived here?' she asked, curiosity getting the better of her.

He shook his head. 'I was away at school. Not far away, but far enough. Then I did a stint with the RN.'

'The what?'

He laughed. 'Royal Navy.'

'I see.' She sat back to digest this piece of information.

'Do you see, Riva, do you really?' he asked without expression. 'I wonder.'

He abruptly skirted the topic of his own career to date and began to probe Riva about hers, but she kept her answers vague without actually departing from the truth. If people knew who her father was she would be back in the same old situation, failing to be taken at face-value, having to fit in with what people expected from the daughter of a man who was a regular feature at the Oscar awards. She doubted whether Richard would himself have heard of Maxwell Hammond. He didn't look the movie-going type, being too restless, too much akin with the great outdoors to spend time in what he no doubt regarded as idle entertainment. But if he didn't recognise the name, somebody in the village would, and she just didn't want the hassle.

'Where were you at school?' he asked in his forthright manner. He'd already told her about the isolated boarding school in Cumberland where he had been sent at the age of eight.

'I've been to plenty of schools,' she told him with a grin. 'I even boarded for a few years, but I hated it and begged to be let out. I suppose travel has been my real education.'

'Father in the armed forces?' he asked casually.

She shook her head. 'No. He just travels and makes money,' she replied briefly. 'He's all right.

I get on well with him. He's been my only family since mother died when I was twelve.' She cast around for a way of changing the subject and Richard seemed content to let her off the hook.

The rest of the meal passed amiably enough, neither of them confiding too much, but respecting each other's privacy as if by tacit agreement.

It was three o'clock by the time they parked the car on the staithe. Bearing in mind what Richard had said about getting straight back to the office to make a few calls, she quickly unfastened her seatbelt and reached for the door.

'Wait!' A hand shot out, staying her own over the catch. She felt a trickle of excitement run up her spine, the way she had when his body had skimmed hers in the car park at Northern Sports. Taking a deep, controlling breath, she half turned, expecting him to release her and mention something about work, but his hand remained where it was, clamped over her own, warm, strong—and no accident, she realised when she looked up into his eyes.

His face was only a few inches from her own. For a long moment she was aware of the drumming of their heartbeats. Then with mesmerising slowness he lowered his face against hers, resting his cheek gently against her own. He didn't move. She felt her mind reel. Waves of heat seemed to sweep up her body like blind energy. It seemed to bring a sense of urgent life to the very roots of her hair. Somehow she resisted the impulse to squirm against him.

With a small groan he lifted his head at last and looked deeply into her eyes. 'I want to take you to bed. Now,' he told her, his voice rasping with emotion. 'Riva. . .' The rest of what he was going to say was muffled as his lips crushed down over her own. She felt her mouth open, all the waves of desire sweeping through her gathering suddenly in that one focus of pleasure as his tongue probed hungrily into the moist, hot centre. Then with a jerk of her head she moved back out of his embrace.

'Don't, Richard.' She felt dismay at the way her respect for him had vanished in an instant. 'You're a married man, remember?' Her eyes glinted scornfully and she felt her hands raise defensively should he ignore her and force another kiss on her.

'Your lips are still willing,' he murmured, tracing the line of them with a touch that was as light as a bird's feather and eliciting a little tremor of desire from her mouth.

'How can you do this? Marriage vows obviously mean nothing to you!'

'Marriage is a mere technicality,' he replied, his eyes like ice.

With a muffled cry she pushed the catch on the door and slithered out before he could move. 'Run your life as you think fit,' she spat, 'but keep me out of it!'

A blush of humiliation staining her cheeks, she made off across the staithe and marched on up the high street towards the office, fighting down her inclination to tell Richard Palmer what he could do with his job and resisting the urge to go straight back to the safety of Sea View instead.

CHAPTER THREE

WHEN Richard followed Riva into the office a few minutes later she was already hard at work and didn't look up. He went straight through into the workroom and she could hear him talking to Ronnie. Obviously their success went down well for she heard a whoop of victory from within. He came back out and went into his own small room off the main one without a word. She heard him pick up the phone. Then, as he'd predicted, he was busy for the rest of the afternoon. When it was time to go she cleared up her things and, avoiding Richard's room, popped her head round the door of the workroom.

'Goodnight, Ronnie.'

He was hard at work, but looked up with a grin. 'Great news, eh?' She nodded. 'See you in the morning,' he called after her as she went out.

She was frowning as she walked back down the high street towards Sea View. She hadn't said goodnight to Richard and she hadn't wanted to. It was so insulting to imagine he thought she'd be grateful for a few stolen kisses. What he had said too burned like a hot coal through her mind. Did he seriously expect her to leap into bed with him just like that? What had she done to create such an impression? Nothing, as far as she could see.

Of course she found him attractive, but only after Mr Hargraves' secretary had drawn her attention to the fact! What was different from one raunchy guy and another? Except that some were married and some were not? She'd seen enough of that kind of life in the past among her father's friends and had no wish to be part of it. It was mildly shocking to realise that human beings were no different here from in Hollywood. Men! she thought with disgust, as she let herself into the cottage. Blue-eyed men in particular. They seemed to think they had it made!

She didn't feel hungry after the lunch of roast beef and Yorkshire pudding Richard had bought for her, and she nibbled on a piece of cinnamon toast as she sat by the sitting-room window looking thoughtfully out at the sea. She didn't have to go back to SeaGear Designs if she didn't want to. She owed them nothing.

Her glance strayed over the quay to the beach. It had obviously been a welcome change in the weather for everyone. Children still played on the strip of sand left bare by the outgoing tide and she watched a group of them building sand-castles.

She got up and when she came back to her perch with a fresh cup of coffee the children were just getting ready to go. A dark-haired woman was shouting something to them from the top of the steps. She made a grab at one of the boys as he came running up to the top, missed, then pursued him, shouting irritably as he dodged out of reach. He ran off along the staithe towards the row of cottages at the far end and Riva watched as the woman, giving up the chase, walked slowly after him. By the sag of her shoulders she looked rather fed up with life. The other children dispersed their separate ways.

Riva was about to transfer her attention to the arrival of a brightly painted fishing boat when she stopped and leaned forward. The woman had caught up with the child who had been giving so much trouble and together they were turning in at one of the cottages. It was the one with the yellow door. The one Richard had visited the other day when he'd told her he was going to have a word with his wife.

So that was Linda. The little boy must be Tom. Now that she thought about it, he had the same dark hair as Richard. That was nothing unusual around here, where dark hair was the norm, but still it seemed obvious enough. The boy would be about nine or ten.

The proximity of Richard's little family in a cottage so close to her own made it seem somehow worse, what he had done and said in the car, though she knew that was illogical. It was wrong however near or far they were.

She took a good long look at herself in the bathroom mirror before she went to bed. Did she look like a girl searching for love on the sly? She hoped not. She would make sure there would be no ambiguity when she turned up for work next morning. Protective camouflage was what was needed. And if Mr Richard Palmer proved too persistent she would hand in her notice.

But when she got in next morning, hair scraped sensibly back into a no-nonsense chignon and a plain navy blue sweater concealing her curves, there was no sign of Richard. Instead Ronnie came bounding through from the workroom as soon as he heard the door. 'The cat's away, now the mice can play!' he sang out. 'Fancy a cup of coffee, beautiful?'

'Where's Richard?' she asked, peering towards his office.

'Chasing up builders. He's trying to sweet talk them into converting the stable block into a factory overnight. He'll probably do it too, knowing him.'

'Good at sweet talk, is he?' she asked drily.

'Haven't you discovered that yet?' He gave her an amused grin. 'He must be slipping these days. Now if I thought you were in the market for a toyboy——'

'Ronnie. Please behave!' Obviously the chignon and the sensible sweater were having no dampening effect whatsoever. 'Now, tell me,' she went on briskly, 'what stable block? What builders? And, most of all, what factory?'

'Ooh, you are efficient!' Ronnie pretended to be impressed. 'Surely he's told you of his plan to house a team of slaves at the Crag?'

'He mentioned getting some machinists in, yes,' she replied. 'But what's this Crag?'

'You don't know the Crag?' Ronnie looked as if she'd claimed the earth was flat. 'The folly of Scarswick? Our late, lamented ancestral home? Ancient seat of the Palmer dynasty? I'm surprised he hasn't given you a conducted tour. Plenty of nice dark corners there——'

'I'll ignore that last remark as it seems too deep to take in at this time in the morning,' she began severely. 'Are you saying he's going to be out all day?'

'No such luck. He'll be coming in to tighten the thumbscrews around lunchtime. But if it's work you're fretting about he's left you a list on your desk. Honestly,' he added as she picked it up and began to scan it, 'you're nearly as bad as he is when it comes to clocking on.'

'Hard work never did anyone any harm,' she reprimanded, knowing that whatever she said it would have little effect on the irrepressible Ronnie.

To her surprise he started back in the direction of the workroom almost at once. 'No fun in partying by yourself. I guess I may as well climb back into the slave ship. Come and unshackle me before nightfall.'

'Here.' She placed a cup of coffee beside the machine a few minutes later. Typically, he had forgotten he'd put the kettle on and the alcove where they made drinks was full of steam. 'And what's this about ancestral homes, then? Where is this place?'

'You can't have missed the entrance gates. Up

at top end. Couple of eagles poised for attack on either pillar? Actually I think they're meant to be ravens, but they're out of scale times a hundred if so. The house is at the end of the drive. You can see it from the beach when the tide's out. The stable block has been empty for years. It's ideal for what we want. Anybody can see that. It just takes a bulldozer like Rich to make it all materialise.'

'Yes. It would.' She could understand Ronnie perfectly now. 'You probably need a bulldozer, Ronnie.' She gave him a wry glance and nodded towards the pile of work waiting to be done.

'Don't be mean to me, Riva. It's bad enough being in disgrace and having them send me home like a bad boy with Richard waiting for me wielding a shot-gun——' He broke off and gave her a sheepish look. 'Has he told you?'

She frowned. 'What about?'

'Me.'

'No. He hasn't mentioned you.'

'Just like Richard. No washing your dirty linen in public. Well, I'm not ashamed.' Despite his words he still looked a little sheepish, and Riva guessed his words sprang from a feeling of defiance rather than anything else. This suspicion was confirmed when he went on. 'I was chucked out of school last term. Richard was livid. He's forcing me to work for SeaGear to keep me on the straight and narrow.' He laughed. 'He's got a hope. If I really wanted I'd be off like a shot.' He gave her a pleased smile. 'But it's going to be a damned good enterprise. Even I can see the potential. When things really get under way there's going to be a lot of travel and a whole lot of fun to be had!'

'So you're in disgrace, are you? In that case you'd better not let me interrupt you any longer!' She made her way back to her desk. She didn't know what Ronnie had done to get himself thrown out of school, but she could imagine Richard taking over the parental responsibilities himself. He seemed to have had plenty of practice.

At around half-past twelve he flew into the building for a few minutes and Riva smiled to herself as she remembered Ronnie's description of the purpose for his return. 'Go and have some lunch, Riva,' he ordered as he swept out again after briskly scribbling his signature at the bottom of the letters she had typed up for him that morning. The door slammed. 'Yes, Mr Palmer, no, Mr Palmer, three bags full, Mr Palmer,' she muttered under her breath, unaware that Ronnie had come into the room.

'Rebellion at last. I was beginning to think you were too good to be true. Well?' he laughed when he saw her embarrassed glance. 'Shall we obey orders? They do a neat pub lunch at the Crab and Lobster.'

She nodded. 'Why not? He can't complain about that, can he?'

She didn't bother with a coat as the warm weather seemed to be holding and together they made their way down to the pub on the staithe. 'I haven't been in here yet,' she told him, ducking her head underneath the lintel and looking round the murky bar for a seat.

'It gets noisy at night when the chaps tank up while they wait for the tide,' he told her. 'You've probably heard them singing.'

'The fishermen?' She nodded.

'Tough bunch,' he added approvingly. His glance scanned the groups dotted at separate tables around the bar and he nodded to one or two. They were all men, she noticed.

While they tucked into doorstep wedges of bread and ham salad Ronnie enlarged on the reasons why he was glad he was out of school at last. 'It was nearly my last term, that's what was so galling to begin with,' he told her, 'but as I'd junked my chances of getting decent grades anyway it was the best thing that could have happened, in retrospect.'

She guessed he was the type who always looked on the bright side. It was an endearing quality, but she could imagine how irritating it must be to someone with the sort of ambition Richard seemed to have. Nothing but first rate would do for him. She was dying to find out why he was only starting out in business at his age. He wasn't as young as his enthusiasm seemed to suggest, and she wondered what had happened in those early years to keep his undoubted ambition under wraps. But, reluctant to ask what might seem too pointed a question about Richard himself, she asked instead why it was he and not his father who had wielded the shot-gun.

'I assume you were talking about a metaphorical shot-gun,' she added with a laugh.

Ronnie looked sombre and there was a sort of bitterness in his eyes when he said, 'Don't count on it. You don't know Richard. He's not all sweetness and light by a long chalk——'

'I never thought he was! I've seen him come into the office like a bear with a sore head——'

'He's got his reasons,' Ronnie hinted, changing tack, 'but he can be a hard devil when he wants. Ever since Dad kicked the bucket last year he's taken it on himself to hold the reins for us all.'

'You mean for you and his wife and son?'

'Them as well. But we've got three sisters. Two safely married and one running wild at college.' He grinned disarmingly. 'Since he came back he's started to treat us like a full-time job.'

'Sounds to me as if you are! I'm beginning to sympathise with him. They're all older than you, then?'

'Yeah—I'm the baby of the family!' He gave her a cheeky grin. 'How old do you think I am, Riva?'

'Nineteen?'

His smile broadened in delight. 'Seventeen,' he corrected, preening a little bit when she couldn't conceal her surprise.

Suddenly he glanced over her shoulder and his expression changed. It was like a hand wiping away all the precocious confidence on it, and all at once he looked scarcely more than fifteen, let alone seventeen. He uttered a curse under his breath and tried to push the glass of whisky he had ordered for himself to one side. Riva felt a shadow loom over her and a hand came out, yanking him off his feet and dragging him towards the door. There was a quickly stifled burst of ironic applause at this show of strong-arm stuff from the group of lunchtime drinkers and Riva swivelled in time to see Richard carting a helpless Ronnie into the street.

By the time she'd joined them the boy was standing with his back against the pub wall, hands thrust defiantly in his pockets, scowling up at Richard whose expression was blacker than anything Riva had ever seen. As soon as she appeared he swung to confront her.

'What the hell do you think you're doing? Plying him with whiskies! Have you taken leave of your senses?'

'Just a minute——'

But Ronnie interrupted. 'Leave Riva out of it. She didn't know I was under age. It was all my idea——'

'Shut up! I've heard enough from you!' Richard turned on him, his brow furrowed with rage, and for a moment she thought he was going to strike him.

'Wait!' She sprang forward. 'What's so awful about having a drink and a sandwich? It *is* lunchtime, after all, and——'

Richard gave her a withering glance. 'He's

broken the law once too often. So mind your goddamned business. Get back to the office.' He started to turn away, but Riva flung out a hand, grasping him by the elbow.

'Am I to understand that was an order, *Mr* Palmer?'

His cold blue eyes scanned her face and something in it must have made him realise he had over-stepped the mark. 'Please, Riva. Do me a favour, let me handle it.' He glared at Ronnie over her shoulder. 'We'll sort this out in private. Go back to the shop with Riva if she'll be kind enough to escort you. I have something to say to the landlord.' He shook off her hand and went to the door of the pub, bending low to get inside.

'Come on then, fella. Let's do as the lord and master says.' She slipped her arm in his,

'You know what he's doing now,' muttered Ronnie bitterly as he reluctantly watched Richard disappear inside. 'He's getting me banned.'

'If the law says you're under age, then that's that, isn't it?' she said reasonably.

'The law!' Ronnie kicked a pebble and began to walk along beside her.

'From what Richard was saying that's an opinion that's already landed you in trouble.'

Ronnie sighed deeply. 'Hell, Riva, you'll be on my side, won't you? He turns everybody against me.'

'He must have had some good reason for saying what he did——' she began.

'So I got into a spot of trouble with a girl from

the village near school. But it was all sorted out.'
He gave her a defiant glance. 'I was feeling pretty
screwed up about it all, so I decided to borrow a
car and go for a bit of a spin one night. No big
crime——'

'Borrow?'

'I honestly intended to take it back.'

'But?'

'God, you're as bad as he is! It wasn't my fault.
I sort of got it written off a bit. But nobody was
hurt.' He quickened his pace. 'It was just bad luck
it happened so soon after the other thing. Now
he's making me keep to the strict letter of the law.
It's not even as if he's whiter than white. To hear
him talk you'd think he'd never done anything
wrong in his life!'

They had reached the shop now. Riva inserted
her key in the lock as Ronnie seemed to be too
concerned with the injustices done him to bother
looking for his own key.

'He's being strict with you for your own good,'
she said lamely as they went inside. Personally she
wondered if Richard's approach was the right one
with someone like Ronnie. His autocractic
manner had made her own hackles rise once or
twice, and Ronnie was a lively boy with a lot of
pride. As much pride as Richard himself, she
thought, struck by the similarity between the two
as they had stood glowering at each other like a
couple of wild animals outside the pub.

Richard came in almost straight away and,
obviously trying to avert the worst of his elder

brother's rage, Ronnie was already hard at work again. Riva couldn't help feeling sorry for him. She watched as Richard went purposefully into the workroom, closing the door firmly between them.

Feeling that, despite the way her sympathies had been aroused, none of it was any real concern of hers, she was hard at work when Richard came back into the office a little later. She felt his eyes on her and reluctantly looked up when he went on standing over her.

'You think I'm a bastard, don't you?'

She lowered her glance. 'It's not for me to have an opinion on your private life,' she told him.

'But you do, don't you?' he replied fiercely.

'I am human,' she remarked, engaging his glance and refusing to lower hers first. 'You might try remembering other people have feelings too.'

'Are you talking about what happened in the car?' he demanded bluntly, holding her glance, but when she didn't waver being the first to turn away.

'Not entirely,' she said to his back. 'But yes, that reflects your whole attitude to people, doesn't it? "*I* want this. *I* want that." You seem to think people are around for the sole purpose of fitting in with your wishes.'

'If only they were,' he rejoined feelingly. 'Life would be a very simple and beautiful thing.' There was a glint of something like humour in his blue eyes as he turned to look at her. But she wasn't in the mood for succumbing to charm of any kind.

'To be frank, Mr Palmer,' she said rather formally, 'I don't care a damn about you or your problems. But I do feel sorry for Ronnie. He sounds as if he's had a raw deal. Now if——' She was just about to say that she would finish her day's work then possibly relinquish her employment with him when he put both hands on either side of the typewriter and glared down, his face only a few inches from her own.

'Do you mean to tell me you think he should have got off scot-free after getting a fifteen-year-old girl into trouble? After writing off a brand-new uninsured sports car which he "borrowed" from a car sales showroom after drinking half a bottle of his headmaster's best brandy? What could the school do but chuck him out? And what was *I* supposed to do? Pat him on the head and tell him what a good boy he was?'

Riva was silent for a moment. Then she said, 'All right, I take your point.' She sighed and looked away. 'He seems so good-hearted underneath it all. It's easy for one mistake to lead to another.'

'Coupled with a complete lack of parental guidance. . .' he added drily '. . .yes, I can see he's almost blameless.'

'I didn't say that. But you mustn't be too hard. If you always treat him in that high-handed way——'

'When?'

'When you dragged him out of the pub in front

of everyone just now. It must have been dread-
fully humiliating for him——'

'Especially as he was trying so hard to impress
you.'

Riva blushed. She hadn't liked to admit to
herself what had been only too obvious. Richard
went on leaning over her, his eyes thoughtful, and
she thought he was going to pursue that line, but
he straightened up and said, 'He got on the wrong
track after Dad died. I guess he took it rather
hard. But he was away at school and I suppose
nobody really talked it out with him. I was with
the RN. My efforts were concentrated on simply
staying alive at that time, I remember. Whatever
was going on here seemed fairly unimportant. The
girls, bless them, were too young themselves to
take responsibility for a wild little lad not much
different from themselves.' He paused. 'When it
eventually got through to me what was happening
back home I got out as soon as I could. Had to
buy myself out of a good career.' He confessed
this last without bitterness, adding, 'Family comes
first, doesn't it?'

He sighed and went to stand by the window. 'I
haven't done too well, have I?'

'There's no point in apportioning blame. These
things happen.'

'No, you're right. I've seen that look in your
eyes. I'm an arrogant bastard, always have been.'
He turned to look at her and his eyes were bright.
'Hell!' He suddenly glanced at his watch. 'You

don't happen to speak French as well as type, do you?'

Surprised by the swift reverse into business mode, she could only nod.

'Very well or merely tourist?'

'Well enough for most things,' she admitted, remembering the year in a French school she had once had.

'I'm expecting a call from a French importer within the hour. Accept the call and check out whether his English is good enough to do business. I expect it is. But if not I'd like you to make it a three-way event.' He nodded to the phone on her desk. Then, as if suddenly recalling something, he came over to her and leaned down. 'Please, Riva. . .Miss Hammond—if you would be so kind?'

'That's better, Mr Palmer.' Their eyes locked and she was compelled to add, 'I was just about to hand in my notice. You've been saved by the skin of your teeth.'

Richard pretended to mop his brow, but his eyes held an extra glint in them and she knew he was taking her criticism of him as seriously as he could.

CHAPTER FOUR

'You speak it like a native,' Richard observed afterwards as he came into Riva's office and sat on the end of her desk. 'You must have gone to a damned good school.'

'Local one, actually. I was the only English child there. It was either sink or swim. At ten you generally choose to swim!' Her eyes were veiled. Nobody had ever complimented her on the skills she'd picked up out of sheer necessity. Her father always took it for granted she would cope with everything. That was what she had been designed for. Richard expected the same. But at least he recognised the fact. He seemed reluctant to leave and she waited, wondering what else he had on his mind.

'I hate encroaching on your time, Riva. But you know me—it's work and sleep and nothing much else. And I tend to think everybody else is the same. . .'

'Go on.' She couldn't help smiling at this new, diffident Richard.

'I wondered if you'd mind coming up to the Crag with me as soon as you've finished those letters. I've got to sort out one or two things before the builders start work on Monday. I'll stand you supper afterwards.'

'Richard, I don't mind helping you in any way I can, during office hours. But I can't get involved socially with you. It's not my style to—look, we've already been through this. You know how I feel.'

'I think maybe we could discuss it.'

'No.'

'Over dinner. You don't know the whole story.'

'I shan't change my mind.' Already she felt herself ready to listen to him, blocking out the danger it might lead to, but still unwilling to let him see how she was wavering.

'It's an innocent enough request—supper at the Crag?' he went on. 'What do you imagine I'm going to do?'

'I simply can't see the point,' she told him, averting her glance.

'See it as a thank-you for all the help you've given me so far. I've already told you I don't know what I'd have done without you.'

Feeling she had no option, she gave a brief nod. 'Supper, then. But I can't stay late.'

'Of course not.'

She looked up quickly, but his expression was serious. 'I mean it, Richard. I'm not going to get involved. Besides, I shall be leaving here soon. There's even less point in. . .' She paused and licked her lips, which were unaccountably dry.

'In?' he prompted.

'In anything,' she finished, getting up abruptly and going over to the filing cabinet and stuffing a sheaf of letters in at random. With her back to him she heard him slide off the edge of the desk.

Footsteps moved over the wooden floor to the door. Only when the door closed did she turn round. It was stupid to feel so breathless at the thought of supper with Richard Palmer. Maybe she had a secret addiction to playing with fire? So long as she knew that was what she was doing, she would be safe.

It was nearly five by the time they climbed the bank to the top end of the village and, sure enough, just as Ronnie had described, there were the eagle-crested pillars and the drive behind a tumbling grey stone wall. They walked in silence towards the house.

'Ronnie tells me you're having the stable block converted into workshops,' she said to break the ice.

'That's the general idea. I want to see what you think about the lay-out. I want it to be a pleasant environment, not like some Victorian sweat-shop. A second opinion will help. Especially a female one, as most of the workers will be women.'

She wondered why he couldn't seek his wife's opinion, but refrained from saying anything. 'How many people do you think you'll have to employ?'

'We'll have to start off with half a dozen and take it from there. With this French order we're really going to have to pull our fingers out. Outlets on the Riviera were more than I'd hoped for at this stage.'

'Your designs are brilliant, Richard.' She wanted to tell him she hadn't seen such good products in Jamaica, but thought it might lead to too many questions. Instead she asked, 'How did you hit on the idea in the first place? Have you done much wind-sailing yourself?'

He gave her a strange look. 'I suppose I've done a fair bit,' he admitted grudgingly. 'Here and there.'

'I suppose you would, being in the navy.' She laughed.

As they approached the stables she saw that they were large and rambling and would once have catered for a number of carriage horses. Now they were in a poor state, the slate roof, though mostly intact, having several gaps in it as well as a lot of missing tiles.

They pottered around for a while, Richard outlining for her the changes he wanted to make. She warmed to his enthusiasm, succumbing as she well knew to the natural charm of his manner so clearly evident when he wasn't trying to lay down the law or play the heavy father to Ronnie. Finally he led her towards the main house. It was gloomy. Elms clustered on the landward side and she knew the garden on the other side led straight to the edge of the cliff.

'Surely nobody lives here, do they?' she asked in surprise as he pushed open the door and walked in. A clutter of boots and waterproofs lay scattered about in the brown and blue Victorian tiled hall and there were bits and pieces lying around that she recognised as parts of a sailing-boat. It was a real masculine clutter.

Ahead was a wide stairway leading to the upper floors, its deep red carpet so worn that the brown undercarpet showed through. It was all spotlessly clean, but everywhere were signs of lack of money and of the particular care of a woman's hand. Riva longed to put everything to rights, for potentially the place had an air of elegance just waiting to be brought back to life.

Richard had ignored her question as if he felt there was no answer necessary and he pushed her on into a large country kitchen. 'I can do you fish, baked, fried or grilled—fresh off the boats this morning,' he added, going over to a rack, 'and a selection of—shall we say a macédoine of vegetables?' He grinned when he saw her expression. 'What's the matter? Don't you think I can cook? It's part of any basic survival course. I'm a dab hand at catching fish with a pointed stick. Not much use in catching the things if you can't also make them taste edible.'

'Richard, stop a minute—do you mean to say you actually live here?'

'Where did you think I lived?'

She shook her head, the ramifications of what he was telling her bursting in with a sudden thud. 'But your wife?' she asked weakly.

'I told you we needed to talk.'

'I've made one or two assumptions about you, haven't I?' She sat down on one of the wooden kitchen chairs and put her head in her hands. Then she looked up at him. 'But you did say you were married.'

'And I also told you it was a technicality. I didn't mean it the way it probably sounded. I take marriage as seriously as anybody. Maybe more so. And in a technical sense I'm not free. In every other sense the marriage is most definitely over. We haven't lived together for years.' He sat down opposite her on the other side of the table. 'Forgive me if I sound vague. It was a very slow drifting apart after the first year.'

She found it difficult to equate his passionate approach to life with anything as lukewarm as the phrase drifting apart seemed to imply. There were a hundred questions she wanted answering. He got up and went over to the old-fashioned stone sink in one corner where there was a parcel of fish on the draining-board. 'Did we decide how we were going to have this?' He seemed strangely diffident and Riva wondered if she'd got him entirely wrong. Only the memory of his muttered words in the car yesterday afternoon made her pause.

'Fish, Riva?' he prompted, looking over his shoulder.

'As you're such an expert,' she said lightly, trying to pull herself together, 'I'll leave that to you.'

'What a cop-out,' he muttered under his breath. 'Fancy chopping a few vegetables, then?'

She got up. 'Do you do this every evening after work?' she asked.

'No. I take it in turns with Ronnie and we always make sure we eat out at least once a week.

He gets plenty of invitations from friends—the attraction no doubt being the notoriety value he's acquired—but those are strictly rationed until I'm sure he's toeing the line.'

'So he lives here with you. Just the two of you?' she asked.

'Haven't been able to lure anyone in to look after us so far,' he joked.

'I'm sorry about this lunchtime,' she said with a little frown. 'I didn't understand the situation at all.'

'No reason why you should. I just don't want him making the mistake I did. It's all very well pretending to be easygoing about it all and saying, as some do, that he's got to learn the hard way—but the hard way can sometimes be a lesson that eats a large chunk out of your life.'

He seemed about to go on to explain what he meant when there was a sound of a cheery whistle in the hall and a few seconds later Ronnie himself poked his head round the kitchen door.

'No smell of cooking yet? Come on, you two, you're slacking. I've rushed back specially to sample your home cooking, Riva.'

'I'm not getting a look in with the master chef in attendance.' She smiled across at him. The animosity that had existed between the two brothers seemed to have vanished completely. Ronnie came over and tried to give a hand with the vegetables.

'Don't do that, kid. Go and pour the adults a nice drink instead.'

'And what about the new generation?' Ronnie was halfway to the door already. 'Don't they deserve even a tiny dry sherry?'

Richard gave him a warning glance. When he returned almost at once he placed the two drinks for Richard and Riva on the kitchen table within reach of them. 'I hope somebody up there is making a note of all this,' he said, raising his eyes heavenwards.

'Let's not go to extremes. You know it's not illegal at home.' Richard's glance followed Ronnie out of the room. 'He's got to learn to hold his liquor and I'd rather he did it at home. . .I know he's not a bad kid. . .'

'Don't worry about him, Richard. He obviously idolises you and I beleive he's really trying to do it right this time.'

'Enough of him—what was I saying?' But Ronnie was breezing back in and there was no opportunity to carry on where they had been interrupted.

The meal was delicious and Riva complimented Richard extravagantly, vibrantly aware of how their eyes kept meeting across the table. Whether Ronnie was aware of it too she couldn't tell, but as soon as the meal was over he made some joke about having to catch up on his homework and took himself off.

'Is he all right?' she asked, not wanting him to feel left out.

'He's got a car in pieces in one of the garages. We'll go out and have a look later. Now, Miss

Riva Hammond,' he reached out for her as she stood up to clear the table, 'where were we?'

'You were telling me about learning things the hard way,' she reminded, 'and the mistakes you've made.'

'No, I don't mean just now, I mean yesterday afternoon.' He brought her pulsing body right up against his own, crumpling her in his arms before she could protest. 'I'd just told you what I wanted to do with you—and you were just about to say yes. . .' he prompted.

Riva shuddered against him. 'I don't remember that part of it,' she breathed, trying to draw back, then feeling her body make an alternative decision that sent her trembling into his arms. His hands were smoothing the muscles of her back, erasing all the tension, making her senses swim. When one hand reached the nape of her neck and tilted her head back she held her breath, willing him to change his mind, knowing that nothing would ever be the same if she let him kiss her. But before she could summon up the will to resist his lips were coming down slowly over her own, pushing her lips apart, melting against hers, spinning her mind into another orbit. His tongue probed heatedly into her mouth. For a long moment there was no sound in the room until at last with a small groan he slowly released her. He stepped back.

'I'm not thinking straight,' he muttered, running one hand through his hair. The blue eyes were hazy. 'Do you always kiss like that?'

'You make it sound as if I make a profession of

it——' She broke off and moved back out of range, leaning against the kitchen table for support. Her legs felt shaky, as if she'd just run a marathon. All she could think was she must get away. Out of this house. Away from Richard Palmer. Somewhere safe where she could think. Though what there was to think about. . . Her eyes seemed to have a will of their own, following his every movement as if attracted by some unseen force. With an effort she averted her head.

'Riva,' he said, his voice sounding hoarse and his expression as confused as hers, 'I don't care a damn about what you've done, where you've come from—what you're running from. It's now that matters. I'm coming back to Sea View with you.' He half turned to the jacket that was slung over the back of a chair.

'No, Richard!' That was the last thing she wanted. And how could he even suggest such a thing with Linda and his son only a few doors away? What he had told her about his marriage might be true, but it still didn't alter the hard facts. 'I don't think any of this is a good idea. I think I'd better go. I shouldn't have let you kiss me like that. It—it was—it took me completely by surprise.'

He gave a disbelieving laugh. 'Listen, I've already told you, I won't pry. Whatever your secret is, keep it. It's safe from me. I'd rather not know. But the rest of it is very clear and above board—I want you like crazy. And you want me.

What could be simpler?' He reached out suddenly, running a hand down the side of her body, observing the rapid in and out of her breath with satisfaction. He moved closer. 'Don't let's waste time playing games——'

'Don't touch me like that. You've got me completely wrong, Richard. I'm not looking for an affair—and I can't forget the fact that you're still married. Naturally you'd have a way of talking it into nothing. Isn't that what married men do? I wouldn't know. I've never——'

'Never been kissed by one before?' he murmured, moving closer still. 'Then it's about time you started with this one.'

He brought her body against his own, the sailor-blue eyes glittering over her face, the lips that had played such havoc with her emotions a few moments ago prepared to do the same again. With a choking sound of protest she pushed at his broad chest, expecting him to yield, and when her hands encountered only solid muscle she wriggled in his arms, trying to break their hold. Instead of freeing her it brought her up more vibrantly against the long length of his body and she raised anger-filled eyes, clipping, 'Let go of me at once!'

He laughed softly and brought his head down against the side of her face. 'Steady, little one, no need to show your claws. We'll take it slower if you want. There's the whole evening ahead of us. . .'

There was something almost protective in the way he held her clasped in his arms with her head buried in the crook of his shoulder and for a moment she was almost persuaded it was going to be safe to remain like that, then something in the tension of his muscles warned her of the dangerous game she was playing. Fire indeed. He was like a volcano, ready to blow its top at the slightest seismographic tremor! She tried to detach herself from the way her senses were shivering with pleasure at the scent and touch and strength of him, and to think only of the facts that warned her to put back her defences.

After a moment or two he lifted his head. 'No.' His eyes half closed as if fighting back some painful spasm. 'No, she says. All right, lady. You win.' He put on a funny accent and reluctantly let his hands trail away from where they had been locked round her, and, stepping back, he stood blinking at her for a further minute as if he couldn't quite believe his eyes.

She put up a hand to smooth back her hair. It felt as if it were flying in all directions.

'I can't get used to living on land,' he said, as if having suddenly worked something out in his mind. He turned away. 'Want to watch television or something?'

He swept up the used crockery left after their meal as he moved across the kitchen, piling the whole lot in a heap into the sink.

'Come on, let's get out of here. It's having a bad effect on my nerves. Fancy a walk? Or what about a stroll down to the Crab and—no, sorry,

that would be like a red rag to the bull——' He
stopped abruptly, narrowing his glance at her.

'Sorry, Riva. Listen to what I'm saying. I never
say sorry, but I'm saying sorry now. When you
live as I've lived over the last ten years you take
what you can when you can get it. If you want
something you don't wait to be asked. You don't
play games. You don't pussy-foot around. Time's
too short. I'm still mentally in that world—tomorrow might never come. Well, it gets to be a habit.
I haven't adjusted to shore life. Forgive me. OK?
Look,' he went on when she didn't say anything,
'what more can I say? Forget it, right? I'm a bull
in a china shop when it comes to love play. For
the sort of women I'm used to, time is money.
OK? For God's sake say something, will you?'

He reached out, yanking hold of her wrist and
dragging her up against him. 'Forgive and forget?
The lady doesn't want to play. All right. That's
your choice. Now just let's forget this ever
happened.'

He dropped her wrist and swivelled to the door.
Despite his mocking humour there was an edge to
his voice that put Riva's thoughts on hold.

What he had just thrown at her was too much
to take in. She had thought she was dealing with
the averagely unfaithful type of male who lived
and set his standards within the limited horizons
of the place he lived, but now she saw him in
another light: a sailor, with a woman in every
port, roaming the high seas for his excitement,
untamed by any shore-based restrictions. A law

unto himself. No wonder his marriage had fallen apart. His wife, if she'd had any sense, would have thrown him out long ago.

It made him even more undesirable. What she wanted, what she had left Jamaica for, was stability. Not this.

Yet his touch still burned through her body, making it ache with the need to be touched again, to be kissed again, to feel his hard body pulsing with desire against her own. . .

She went to the chair and picked up her cardigan, shrugging it on over her shoulders as if for protection. 'Don't see me out. I can find my own way.'

She knew his eyes were on her as she crossed the kitchen and opened the door. Only when she was about to step through did he speak.

'Riva—tomorrow. . . Are you going to come in?'

She turned. 'Oh, yes, Richard. I'll be sitting at my desk as usual. Don't worry, I won't walk out on you just like that—unless you drive me to it.'

He didn't have time to reply. She went out, closing the door quietly behind her.

She made her way over to the stables and found Ronnie lying underneath a car. His face beamed up, covered in grease, when he saw who it was. 'I'm going back home now,' she told him. 'Just called to say goodnight.' He waved a spanner at her as she left.

CHAPTER FIVE

THE weather held and the next morning Riva took one look at the sun before slipping into the sundress she had brought up with her.

If she was really going to stay for a while longer—and that was something she would keep under constant review after last night—she would have to pick up a few clothes from somewhere. Apart from a pile of sweaters and a few shirts to wear with her jeans, she only had one decent dress with her other than the white one she was wearing now. Remembering the dangers that no doubt lay ahead the minute she stepped into the office, she grabbed the big blue cardigan she had worn to such little effect the day before, hoping that if it was slung carefully around her shoulders it would disguise what lay beneath.

There was nothing she could do about her deep, all-over tan. For the first time she realised how startling she must look. Everyone around here was pasty white—except for the out-in-all-weathers fishermen, among whom she counted Richard and Ronnie for the purposes of suntan. They were both nearly as brown as she was. Even Ronnie, with his fair complexion and light brown hair, had a healthy, glowing colour as if he spent long hours out of doors.

She looked longingly back through the shop window at the sunlit street as she let herself in. Richard came through straight away. His manner was abrupt and he didn't look at her. 'You're in good time.' He'd obviously been waiting for her, probably not really expecting her to turn up. She had surprised even herself when she set off up the high street. Only the thought of not wanting to leave the two of them in the lurch—Ronnie's need for stability weighing heavily on her conscience— had seemed to justify the decision.

Before she could even say good morning he went on, 'If you wouldn't mind dealing with a bit of correspondence I've left on your desk, we might as well open up the shop today. This weather's likely to bring in a flood of custom.' He started back towards the inner rooms. 'Let me know when you're ready and I'll show you how the cash register works.' He paused. 'Is that all right?'

'I expect so. Why shouldn't it be?' she asked, suddenly on the defensive.

'Warn me before you leave, won't you? Or should I start looking for a replacement straight away?'

She moved over to the dusty counter and looked round at the shelves of stock, the racks of gaudy wet suits, the chandlery section with its neatly coiled ropes and compasses and unrecognisable bits and pieces for the boating trade. 'Do you think you'll be able to get anyone?' she asked.

'Hopeless, I should think.'

'Then I'd better stay awhile, I suppose.' She avoided his glance.

'I'll never find anyone like you. I don't expect to.' His voice was like brittle ice. 'And you're working for next to nothing. You could obviously be commanding a very high salary indeed. I told you I wouldn't pry. I'm trying to see your arrival as a simple stroke of luck. But good luck never lasts, does it? I don't expect it to. Let's just leave it like that.' He went out.

The day was a pattern for the following weeks, office work first then the rest of the day in the shop. About halfway through the afternoon Ronnie would be allowed out on one of the sailboards in the bay. The first time she saw him leave she noticed he was wearing SeaGear designs.

'I'm a walking billboard for this place!' he quipped as he went into the street. When he returned there were one or two girls trailing after him. Later the shop was full of customers and a party from the youth camp on the cliffs came in asking questions about the sort of equipment suitable for beginners. It was the same, with slight variations, most days after that. The good weather held, and as long as it held the shop was busy. The weekends, instead of being time off, were their busiest period and only when Riva saw she was beginning to get behind with the office side did she suggest getting an assistant in on Saturdays.

'A school-leaver?' Richard frowned. 'Good idea. Can you see to it?'

'All right.' She turned away. He hadn't spoken to her about anything personal since that evening at the Crag and she couldn't resist the acid question, 'Any preference—blonde, redhead or brunette?'

'If I said it was all one you'd no doubt think the worst.' His eyes were chips of blue ice, sweeping her with the soullessness of an arctic gale.

She tossed her head but held her tongue. There was nothing to be gained from wrangling with him. He would take it as evidence of a change of heart.

It was easy to find a Saturday girl—in fact, there were two new faces on the scene for on the second Saturday the girl brought along her best friend and the two of them agreed to share Sundays between them. They even came in to help out now and then after school. Riva was glad of the company for, although they were only sixteen, they were full of fun and an added advantage was that they served to deflect Ronnie's attentions to some extent.

He had started to show all the signs of puppy love, appearing casually on the staithe outside her cottage in the evenings as if just happening to be taking a stroll, and coming through into her office rather more often than his work warranted.

If Richard was aware of his young brother's interest in her he said nothing. The girls, both pretty and dark-haired, thought both men were wonderful and made no secret of the fact, but obviously thought Richard was out of their range. Ronnie though was another matter, and they kept up a constant surveillance of his every movement. His reaction was studiedly cool, either because he was sincerely afraid of Richard's reaction should he step out of line again, or because he imagined he was too sophisticated for them now that Riva was around.

It was at the end of a long day that they all decided to go down to the beach and watch Ronnie test out one of the new sailboards they had added to their expanding list. Business was doing really well, and after a regimen of work, sleep, eat, even Richard seemed to welcome a brief respite.

The sun shone out of a cloudless sky. 'May as well make the most of the weather,' he told Ronnie. 'There'll be storms tomorrow.'

Ronnie nodded. As if Richard's word is law, thought Riva, looking sceptically at the cloudless horizon.

She and the girls leaned on the railings above the harbour wall while Ronnie launched the board. Richard came to stand beside them, blue eyes screwed against the sun. 'It's a good job you've got somebody like him to test the equipment,' observed Riva.

'Yes. I'm so lucky.' Richard's voice was level. He looked down, his glance sweeping her face. 'Give it a try yourself if you like. I'm sure Ronnie wouldn't mind giving you a few lessons.' His mouth tightened. 'No doubt you could handle him without getting in a panic.' He swivelled. 'See you in a while.'

He headed in the direction of the cottage with the yellow door. She tried not to watch to see when he left, but he came out within a few minutes, a young boy straddled over his shoulders. They came down to the group by the railings and Richard swung the boy upside-down under one arm. 'Meet Tom,' he announced. 'Tom, say hello to Sue, Liz and Riva.'

The boy gabbled all their names in one, still hanging upside-down, then begged to be taken out on a sailboard. Richard seemed to hesitate, but only for a moment. 'Come on, then, skipper, let's go and get the gear.' The two of them went off up the street towards the shop. Riva wondered how Richard was going to talk his way out of that. Obviously the child was too young to go out on a board. The sea, though calm enough, was a dangerous place for a youngster.

Ronnie came gliding into the beach just then and they all transferred their attention to him. His face was glowing with exertion. 'Stiff breeze out there,' he called, heaving the now lifeless board out of the water. 'Where's Rich?'

'Gone up to the shop,' one of the girls said.

'He'd love this one. Flies like a bird!' Ronnie was all enthusiasm and came to lean on the railings with them for a moment. Liz went to the ice-cream kiosk and came back with a Coke and some crisps. It was an obvious love-offering for

Ronnie and as he sucked thirstily at the straw Riva wondered if he understood the purpose of it. But Richard was already back.

She turned with a quickly concealed gasp as he came up.

He had changed out of his jeans and open-necked shirt into a SeaGear wet suit. It was one of those with the chopped-off legs, revealing that his tan was a deep bronze and probably as all-over as her own. His thighs, as she had suspected from previous covert appraisals, were all muscle and his legs were so perfectly proportioned that they made her want to reach for a camera. The rubber suit had a shoulder fastening and he did it up now as he exchanged some chit-chat with Ronnie and the girls. Basically it was a black rubber suit he had on, with bands of lime green and bright pink running down the short sleeves, and a couple of bands going horizontally across the chest as if to emphasise its width—as if it needed emphasising, she thought reluctantly—but it clung to every muscle of his body, outlining his perfect shape like a second skin. His dark hair skimmed the high protective collar.

He was pulling on a pair of rubber gauntlets in the same glowing colours, the muscles of his forearms bulging with the movement. Then she saw him reach down and scoop Tom up under one arm. He was dressed in a miniature version of his father's suit, except that it covered his legs and arms. He wriggled like a little fish.

'Let's punch on down, Dad! Come on!' he

yelled in delight. He let his father hoist him along and Richard, having decided to take Ronnie's sailboard out, strode as eagerly as his son across the beach to where it lay.

After the first shock to her senses Riva had managed to pull herself together. He looked fantastic, like a model out of some brochure advertising water-sports holidays. But it was all being done to advertise the company product. No doubt he would merely potter around in the harbour with the boy, creating the maximum visual disturbance to the quiet seaside scene and when he'd got all the attention he wanted he would stroll back, the suit scarcely wet, his silver smile firmly in place.

She nearly turned away. Why should she be a party to his promotional stunts? But curiosity got the better of her. People always made such fools of themselves on sailboards. He would have to be as good as Ronnie not to look a complete idiot in the bouncy waters inside the harbour. She waited.

He was bending down, talking to Tom now, no doubt warning him about the dangers of playing too close to the edge. Then he stepped on to the board, leaving the bright sail bobbing on the surface, one hand round the rope as if intending to pull it up, the other reaching down for his son. Then, so quickly that Riva wasn't quite sure how he did it, he pushed off from the shelving beach, placed the boy neatly in front of him, and lifted the heavy mast to vertical. The huge sail glowed with the delicacy of a butterfly's wing with the sun behind it. Then in a graceful curve the wind caught them, lifting them over the tips of the waves in a long, pure arc towards the harbour exit.

'Beautiful.' It was Ronnie. 'Trust Rich. I always think I'm getting it right. Then I watch him.'

'He must have done this before,' muttered Riva, eyes still riveted on the perfect sight of the coloured sail as it slipped effortlessly beyond the harbour into the deep blue of the open sea.

'Are you kidding?' Ronnie gave a laugh, then he jerked his head round. 'You're serious, aren't you?'

'What do you mean?'

'You really don't know about him, do you?'

'I know some things. What exactly did you have in mind?' she asked irritably.

'My dearly beloved brother,' he said with a laugh, 'was not only Combined Forces Sailboard Champion for umpteen years, he was also captain of the Olympic team in Honolulu. Remember that time we swept the board?'

'Oh.' There didn't seem anything else she could say.

Ronnie's attention turned back to where his brother was performing a series of lazy zigzags across the bay. 'The orders for SeaGear don't just come in because our designs happen to be the best you can buy—people are buying a little bit of Richard Palmer's genius too.' He grinned at the confusion in her face. 'They think it works like magic—touch it, and a little bit of it will rub off on you!'

Liz pushed in between them, obviously thinking Riva had had more than her fair share of Ronnie's attention. 'We thought we'd go and sit on the sea wall to watch,' she informed him. Ronnie allowed himself to be led away, a girl on either arm.

Riva stayed where she was. Everything she learned about Richard seemed to swing her one way or the other. There was no middle ground. No balance. She was pushed either violently for him—or equally violently against.

It was impressive to learn he was so eminent in the international sports world, and his reluctance to brag about it fanned her respect for him. On the other hand she knew all about the beach bums who spent their days roistering in one expensive resort after another. A sailboard was the essential piece of equipment.

She could see Richard slotting easily into that world now. The wild beach parties she had witnessed from the protective cocoon of one or other of her father's villas had had a forbidden fascination.

'Wastrels,' her father's friends had judged, everything in their monied lives resenting the irresponsibility of the young who thronged the beaches and created havoc with their sailboard rivalries. It was probably because they never seemed to do a day's work from one season's end to another—as if life was meant to be one long party—that irked the permanent residents so much. Admittedly the instructors worked hard in the season, patiently showing beginners the ropes, but, taking out the boards themselves as the sun painted the sea with molten gold, their wild whoops of freedom spoilt the sophisticated drinks on the terraces where people like her father and the friends of his generation looked askance.

To be honest Maxwell Hammond wasn't like that—he was too much a vagabond himself to be against them and he would defend them against criticism, a wicked smile on his face as he uttered what he knew was heresy. But she assumed he was only doing it to be provocative.

The sailboard bums were everywhere. Wherever there was sun, sea and sand. They were an inevitable backdrop to whichever resort her father took her to. And wherever they went it was the same story and they were blamed for everything that went wrong in the resorts from noise and disruption to petty crime and bad weather.

Riva had gone along with the general prejudice. She had had to endure the whistles and suggestive banter from them every time she went on to the public beaches. She was glad when they were banned from the ones her father frequented.

Now she clearly saw what type Richard Palmer was. Despite his fond-father act he was just like the others. Irresponsible. A maverick. An outsider to respectable society. She hated him more than ever now. He was definitely off-side. She couldn't imagine why it had taken her so long to learn about him. She supposed it was something to do with the village itself. It was an unexpected backdrop for someone like that—what did Dad call them? Surf cowboys—but she supposed even cowboys had to have a home.

She frowned, eyes still on the coloured triangle as it wove its wild patterns. Clearly he was as mad as all that breed. Witness the fact that he had taken a child out with him in the open sea. There they were, skimming back and forth as if they owned the universe.

She would go back to the cottage now, as work was obviously over for the day. It was time she had some time to herself. There were letters to write. Notes to be made. She hadn't had a single look at her songs since she'd arrived. Now it was time.

Half an hour later she slapped her pen down and got up to switch on the radio. The trouble with Sea View was its view. It was too interesting. Especially now he was back. She couldn't help noticing the arrival of the gaudy triangle in her line of vision. It came to a graceful halt halfway up the beach and she saw him let out the rope holding the mast. It slid smoothly through his fingers as he stepped on to dry land. Tom, she noticed, was clipped on to the board, and Richard bent to snap him free so he could scramble off. So he wasn't as irresponsible as she'd thought. Even so. . .

The dark-haired woman she took to be Linda came down to the harbour steps and waited for the two of them to come up. She snatched Tom's hand at once and made as if to hustle him away, but the boy was still excited about his trip around the bay and hung on to his father's arm as if refusing to go. She saw Richard's hand come out and ruffle the boy's hair. He said something and Tom reluctantly went over to his mother. Linda pulled him by the arm, leading him away.

Richard stood looking after them until the boy turned in at the gate, gave a little wave, then went into the cottage after his mother. Richard went on staring across the staithe for a few minutes longer with a look of unashamed regret on his face then slowly, by himself now, pulled off the rubber gauntlets with the non-slip palms and unzipped the neck of his wet suit. Unlike Ronnie when he returned to land, he seemed as unruffled as when he went out. His powerful shoulders eased themselves inside the tight rubber suit then he made his way back down the beach to dismantle the sailboard.

Driven on impulse Riva found herself outside the cottage, and she was halfway across the beach before she checked herself. But by then Richard had already looked up and seen her.

'I——' One hand flew to her mouth. Recovering, she said, 'I saw you come in. Do you want a hand?'

The weight on his shoulders seemed to lift. His blue eyes warmed, but after that initial quickly concealed response he became businesslike. 'Help me keep this sail out of the sand.' Without further talk they got the fabric free of the mast and folded it in nautical fashion until it was small enough to fit inside its sail bag. 'Done this before?' he asked approvingly as she twisted the mast out of its socket.

'Now and then,' she replied carefully.

'You can use the gear whenever you like, you know. At least—when you've checked out the conditions with me first.'

'Thanks.' She was probably about as good as Ronnie, but she wasn't going to tell him that.

She started to carry the light aluminium pieces of mast up the beach, resting them against the railings when she got to the top. He didn't seem to think there was anything unusual in what she did—he probably had hundreds of willing helpers in the season when the place was thronged with tourists, she thought, wondering why the idea should make her feel so resentful.

They took everything back and stored it in the loft at the shop. He came out with her and she paused while he locked up. He held his old jeans and the rest of his clothes in a bundle underneath his arm. She imagined him going back alone to the Crag, thoughts of his little son Tom still in his mind, the long summer evening stretcing in loneliness ahead of him.

'I'd just made a pot of coffee when I saw you come in. . .' she began, carefully not meeting his eye.

'If that's an offer I'll take you up on it,' he replied at once. 'Assuming you don't mind the party gear.' He indicated the wet suit and short rubber boots.

'It's one of the perks of inviting boardsailers to

afternoon tea,' she quipped, turning at once and refusing to let her glance linger over the flagrantly sexy figure he cut as he stepped after her. Eyes followed them down the street, but she refused to let him guess she noticed them, treating him with a remote politeness, determined not to let him imagine for one minute that her offer included anything other than what she'd told him was on the menu.

'You've changed things,' he said as soon as he stepped inside Sea View. 'More flowers. Books.' He picked one up, flicked a glance at the title and put it down again. 'Very homely,' he judged.

She swept up her notebooks without looking at him. 'Don't tell me you can read as well.'

'As well as what?' he came back swiftly.

He seemed to fill the little sitting-room and she ducked into the tiny kitchen, praying he would stay safely where he belonged. This had been a silly impulse and now she was regretting it.

'As well as what?' he asked softly, coming to stand in the doorway.

He was almost within touching distance.

'As well as run a business, drive a car, play father to a whole host of people and generally——' She stopped, losing her concentration for a moment. 'Isn't that enough?' she asked, touching the side of the coffee-pot to see if it was still hot and stretching for another cup and saucer from the overhead cupboard so she didn't have to look at him.

'I read about two books a year, mostly to do

with sailboarding,' he told her. 'Oh, and there's Reeds, my bible.'

She looked at him over her shoulder with raised eyebrows.

'Tide charts for the UK. That's the one book I keep under my pillow.'

She didn't want to know anything about his sleeping arrangements, but held back from saying so. She was still kicking herself for having invited him in. He was grinning at her like an idiot from the doorway, his amiable, affable, 'butter wouldn't melt in my mouth' look on his face, all charm and sailor-boy blue eyes glinting wickedly as if she were about to offer him a birthday present.

'Can I take anything through?' he asked, coming across the kitchen towards her.

'No!' She stepped sideways, grabbing at the coffee-pot and holding it like a defensive weapon in front of her. 'There isn't a lot of room in here,' she told him. 'It's probably best if you go and sit down out of the way.' For a moment she thought he was going to argue, then with an extra glint in his eye that plainly told her he was reading her discomfort and putting only one interpretation on it he left her to it.

She heard him fiddling about with the radio. Looking for something smoochy? she wondered, as she opened a biscuit tin, poured milk into a jug and generally tried to bring herself to the task in hand.

But when she finally emerged from the kitchen

with the tray he was hunched over the radio
listening in to the weather forecast.

'Heavens, we'll know when it arrives, won't
we? I can never understand this obsession with
the weather in this country.'

'You would if you were planning to go out there
in it.' He indicated the open sea.

'Are you?'

'No. Not in the next three days, according to
this. Unless the worst comes to the worst.'

Not quite sure what he meant by this last
remark, she set the tray down and didn't comment. He was sprawling in the two-seater sofa,
taking up most of it, and when she looked around
for somewhere to sit he made as if to move over,
but she sank quickly down in the armchair opposite, keeping a good distance between their out-
stretched legs beneath the coffee-table.

'This cottage really is only big enough for one,'
she said shakily, suddenly feeling how its walls
had shrunk.

'Beats me how Linda gets on with Tom down
there.' He glanced out of the window.

'Maybe that's all she can afford or something,'
Riva muttered, not wishing to pry into his finan-
cial arrangements with his wife, but compelled to
say something.

'She doesn't have to be able to afford anything.
Not Linda. She has her rights. Always has had,
always will have. Come hell or high water.' He
spoke lightly despite the apparent bitterness of his
words.

'Don't talk to me about her, Richard——'

'I wasn't going to.' He pressed his lips together. 'Taboo subject, sorry. Listen,' he said, deliberately changing the subject, 'I'm going to have to go away soon. Drumming up yet more sales. Are you going to hang on till I get back. Or,' he let his voice lower, 'will I come back to find you've run away?'

'I don't run, Richard. I never have and I don't intend to start now. I'm fully aware of how difficult it would be if I walked out on you at the moment. I've already told you that.'

'I thought you might have changed your mind——'

'I'll let you know in good time if I do. I won't just walk out without warning.'

'Is that my reward for being a good boy?'

His eyes deliberately widened, boy-blue, innocent as the sun. Riva felt a shock like an electric current rush up her body and lodge itself somewhere in the region of her throat with a pulse like a thousand-watt charge.

To change the subject and bring her mind back under control, she said, 'I felt quite worried when I saw you take little Tom out on the board. I didn't realise he had a safety harness on.'

'I'm not stupid,' he observed drily, his eyes still saying something else as his glance lingered over her face.

'I used to see a lot of sailboard bums—with my father when we—when we visited different resorts,' she floundered.

'On holiday, you mean?'

'Us? Oh, yes, holidays, that sort of thing. He called them surf cowboys—they were always causing trouble.'

'So now I'm guilty by association. Sailboarder equals water vandal. I can live with that. Ronnie presumably told you about the respectable side of it all?'

'The respectable Olympic team?'

'Very respectable. No drinking. No late nights. . .and definitely no women. And we said we did it for fun. Oh, well,' he continued, 'I've already guessed I'll never win with you, Riva. I just wish you'd control your eyes, that's all.' He put down his coffee-cup and leaned forward. 'What are they really trying to tell me? That I don't stand a chance—so keep off? Or am I supposed to ignore all that as if it's white noise on a radio channel and listen in to the message underneath? It's coming through loud and clear, Riva. And it's a very different story.'

'You're imagining it,' she said abruptly, putting her cup down and pouring more coffee into it with such haste that it spilled in the saucer. 'You know precisely what I feel. Can we talk about something else?'

'Haven't you noticed something—we're fast running out of things to talk about? This is the taboo list——' he ticked them off on his fingers '—your mysterious past, my marriage in name, your feelings—my feelings. . . Soon there'll be nothing left to say to each other—maybe,' he went on in a changed tone, 'that's when the action can start.'

'There won't be any action, Richard. I don't want that sort of action.' Her voice sounded impossibly tight and high. She stopped talking and averted her head.

'I'm a patient man. The game comes down to this—will you run as soon as the going gets interesting? Are you a coward, Riva?'

'I've told you I never run.'

'What if there are storms in the offing? Will you try and weather them?'

'Storms don't scare me. And I'm not a fair-weather sailor either.' She gave a half-smile, remembering what he had said once before.

He remembered it too and began to laugh softly. 'I don't believe you are. So, as I said, it's going to be interesting—and I'm a patient man when necessary. It'll be interesting to wait and see what you decide to do. . .'

'Well,' she said, getting her voice back under control, 'I do hope you won't be too disappointed. What *I* decide to do won't be anything *you'll* find worth waiting for.'

He laughed darkly. 'Don't be too sure, Riva. Just don't be too sure. . .'

CHAPTER SIX

THE change in the weather Richard predicted came in the middle of the night. Riva was woken up by a regular crashing sound outside and it took her a few minutes to work out what it was. Then she sat bolt upright. It was the sound of tons of water pounding against the sea wall. Getting out of bed, she went over to the window and looked out in time to see a curtain of white rise up like an enormous silent wraith before subsiding with a clatter against the wall. Shivering, she crawled back under the covers, glad to be on dry land and not at sea.

Next morning the sky was blue again, but the sea heaved on the horizon like a badly tamed animal waiting to be set loose.

She donned jeans and a shirt once more, glad to have experienced that brief summer. The shop was open, but it was so quiet that she spent most of the day getting up to date in the office with the adjoining door open so she didn't miss any stray customers. Ronnie was hard at work packing orders and she gave him a hand, ringing the carriers and making arrangements for an overseas shipment. Richard came back from discussions with his architect halfway through the afternoon.

He was in the suit again. Riva couldn't conceal a covert smile.

'So?' He scowled when he saw her face.

'You look so different,' she giggled. 'Is it really yours?'

'I thought you'd approve,' he said, smiling dangerously. 'Makes me look nice and tame, doesn't it?' He came to stand over her and she automatically moved back. 'One of these days, Riva, you'll stand your ground. I've never met anybody so edgy.' He moved away.

'I'm sure you haven't—among the sort of women you claim to fraternise with!' The words came out with rather more venom than she'd intended.

The lightness vanished from his eyes. 'Hell, what a bore. Any messages for me?' he asked, reverting abruptly to business mode.

She shook her head and riffled through some papers on her desk. 'I'm sorry.' She kept her head bent. 'I didn't mean it to come out quite like that.'

'You intended the words but not the spirit?'

She nodded.

'Fair enough.' He draped himself in the doorway. 'Fancy a walk up to the Crag to check out the builders with me? You've been slaving away in this place all day, haven't you?'

'So has Ronnie.'

'He's having the weekend off. He's got to catch up.'

'OK.' She finished what she was doing and joined him in his office a few minutes later.

He was ready to go and as they walked up the bank he said, 'About this weekend—can you and the two girls handle the shop by yourselves?'

Riva nodded. 'Ronnie said you're taking him to some race meeting.'

'It's a long-standing arrangement. He's not allowed to drive on public roads, but he's still allowed on a private race-track. It's one way of getting the driving bug out of his system!' He turned to her. We're staying overnight on Friday and going on from there. 'I'd assumed I would have to shut up shop, but as you're around and if you really don't mind opening up. . .? Would you mind?'

'Not at all. It sounds as if it's in a good cause.' She could just imagine the two brothers—tear-away Ronnie and Richard watching with almost fatherly pride. . . It was so good they could do things together.

'If you get fed up just close it and go home. The weather's going to be fairly changeable and there shouldn't be many people around. No boards to be hired out, that's important. The weather's just not going to be good enough. If anybody takes a board out in the bay this weekend they need their heads examining. That goes for you too, Riva.' He touched her lightly on the arm.

'What makes you think I'd be good enough to sail out there?' she demanded, moving her arm away. 'The seas are too short. I doubt whether I could handle that.'

He laughed. 'It's known as the Scarswick chop.

You have to know something to recognise it.' His eyes trailed curiously over her face. 'Still no go?'

'What?' she asked, irritated by the piercing glance he sent her way.

'Mystery blonde, Riva Hammond. . .' he murmured humorously. 'Don't risk it though, Riva. I mean it. I'd hate there to be an accident.'

'Frightened I'll damage your property?'

'Sure,' he laughed. 'That's my main worry. My property!' He took her arm. The gesture clearly told her there was a double meaning in his words. She knew it was nonsense, but it gave her a warm, protected feeling like the time he'd held her for a moment in the kitchen. But that time she'd warned him off.

Now she didn't warn him. And when his arm brushed hers accidentally as they walked up the bank she didn't flinch away but walked along beside him, allowing the now-and-again touch as they went up to the top.

By the time they approached the stable block the sound of builders could be heard hard at work. 'Ronnie said you'd charm them into rebuilding it overnight,' she smiled. A feeling of happiness was over her. It was good to be involved with something that was obviously going to be a success. Richard seemed pleased with the progress that had been made and the foreman passed the time of day with them until Richard looked at his watch. 'Carry on the good work, Jack. I'll see you before you go.'

He turned to Riva as they went round the side

of the house. 'Come on, let's go back by the cliff path.' She followed him through a gate in the stone wall bringing them out into a narrow lane that wound between the cottages. A few minutes' steep climb brought them out at the top of the cliff.

'It's breathtaking!' she exclaimed when she saw the vista below. The harbour looked like a child's toy. Each cottage huddled next to its neighbour like plasticine models.

They stood side by side for a moment. Richard for once was quiet, no wisecracks, no pointed remarks, and when she stole a look at him he looked away, clambering suddenly on down the steep path, only halting at the first turn to hold out his hand for her. She came skidding light-footedly after him, her cheeks wind-whipped to a glowing pink.

'I wish you didn't look so. . .' He tightened his jaw and turned again, inviting her to follow him. They skidded down to the next turn. Lower now, they were on a level with the grey-tiled roofs, level with the chimneys, one or two of them loosing a mist into the air, filling their nostrils with the scent of woodsmoke. He held out his hand again. This time she took it. He brought his other one up to clasp it against his chest.

'As I was saying,' he began, 'that is, if you want to know what I was saying. . .?'

'I'm not sure. . .' Her hand felt trapped, but it was a comfortable feeling. Again she felt safe.

As if recognising her feeling, he said as if

quoting, '"Put your hand in mine and I will protect you".' He gave a short laugh. 'That's the title of a painting I have hanging in my bedroom. It's been there since I was a child. Maybe one day you'll come up and see it. I can guarantee very few have set eyes on it.'

As if unwilling to provoke a rejection he continued down the lane, still holding her hand, but in a friendly, almost brotherly manner, until they came to an iron gate. 'Short cut through the churchyard. Come and say hello to my ancestors.'

He led her round a number of moss-covered monuments until they came to a plot within an iron railing. She saw that all the names ended with Palmer—Charles, Richard and Henry for the men, Charlotte, Isabel, Anne for the women, with few variations. It gave her a sense of what it must be like to belong to a large family, safely rooted into one spot for generation after generation. She thought of her father's family, the Ravenscrofts, and with a little shock she realised that there might be a grave or two belonging to them.

She began to walk between the rows of stones, some flat, some standing, peering at the names obscured by the ravages of the sea air. Richard followed her. 'What are you doing?'

'I told you when we first met I was from round here,' she told him. 'Well, in a way it's true. At least, I was born in the general hospital in Scarborough, but my dad definitely lived here when he was a boy. His mother was a Ravenscroft.'

Richard looked at her in astonishment. 'Are

you joking?' Taking her by the hand, he led her
to a corner of the graveyard. Ivy trailed in abun-
dance over the broken stones and the air of careful
attention prevalent in the Palmers' plot was
absent. Scratching at one of the lichen-covered
slabs, Richard traced for her the name
Ravenscroft.

She was as happy as if she had won a prize.
'I've never had any real family before—I mean,'
she laughed, 'any sense that I came from
anywhere.'

Richard sat down on one of the stones and
couldn't stop himself from laughing. 'You're
priceless. You know what the Ravenscrofts were,
don't you?'

'What?' She looked puzzled.

'Smugglers, you idiot. For centuries they waged
a war against the law-abiding Palmers. If you stand
on the cliff top you can see how the village houses
are built in two main groups. One side built by the
Palmers—the other by the Ravenscrofts. They say
it was because the Palmers controlled the cliff-top
that the Ravenscrofts turned to smuggling as the
only way of making a living. The Palmers exacted a
toll on everything coming in or out of the village.
The Crag gave them complete control. Your
crowd,' he laughed, 'were a wily bunch and got up
to all kinds of tricks to get their contraband goods
into market.'

Riva was gazing at him in astonishment. 'You're
making this up,' she said at last.

'Check it out in the library at the Crag if you

like. I haven't bothered to read it up, but I'm told it's all there.' He folded her hand in his again and pulled her into the shelter of his arms. 'Your face, if you could see it. . .does family mean so much to you?'

'I've never belonged anywhere,' she told him, head resting against his shoulder. 'It's as if my ancestors have disappeared like grains of sand through the fingers. . .'

She felt his arms come tightly round her, holding her to him in a bear-hug that shut out all insecurities.

When he lifted her head up so he could look into her face there was something in his expression that told her he wanted to say much more than he would allow. They began to walk slowly back towards the main gate.

'What now?' he asked. 'Feel like saying hello to *Sea Maid*?'

'Sorry?'

Without answering, he took her by the arm and led her down a side street towards the inner harbour. There were a dozen boats of different kinds anchored in the lane and a lighter tied up at the foot of the harbour steps. 'In you go,' he told her, bending down to hold the boat steady.

'But what are we going to do? Go for a row around the harbour?' She smiled and stepped lightly into the little wooden boat. Richard climbed in after her and untied it, pushing them out across the water as he unshipped the oars. The outgoing tide and Richard's strong strokes soon pulled them into the middle of the channel and as they swung close to one of the yachts at anchor Riva couldn't help murmuring a warning, though she was sure Richard knew what he was doing. To her surprise he angled their boat across the stern of the yacht and proceeded to tie up.

'Richard——?'

'Don't look so worried,' he laughed. 'We're not an illicit boarding party. This is *Sea Maid*—of the Palmer fleet!'

There was no time to say anything more because he was already climbing up the short ladder at the stern of the yacht and Riva quickly followed him.

'If the tide was right we could go for a sail, but I'm afraid if we go out on the ebb tide we won't be able to get back in till nearly midnight.' He gave her a look that hinted he wouldn't mind at that, but seeing her own expression he added, 'We'll make a day of it as soon as we can if you'd like to?'

Riva nodded. 'That would be terrific. It's ages since I've done any sailing——' She broke off, realising she had laid herself open to more questions, but Richard, if he noticed, didn't take her up on it. Instead he removed the hatch board and went below, calling back over his shoulder, 'I'll fix a cup of coffee while you have a look round, then I've got to turn the engine over a few times.' He disappeared into the cabin and Riva sat out on deck, revelling in the sudden sense of freedom she got from feeling the sea beneath the boat. It would be heavenly to sail off into the blue with a man like Richard.

His voice broke into her reverie calling her down into the cabin and she climbed down with a little smile of contentment round her lips. Richard looked up casually from his position in the tiny galley then did a sort of double take. 'Your hair's all ruffled,' he said huskily, taking half a step forward.

The movement, small though it was, was enough to bring them up close to each other so that all he had to do was reach out with one hand to touch her wind-whipped cheeks. There was a world of tenderness in his voice that made her draw in her breath. When he looked at her with those blue eyes of his, the humour in them giving place to something much more disturbing, she was powerless to resist.

'Riva——' he muttered, reaching for her. Without either of them saying anything more they found themselves in each other's arms. She shivered as his hands caressed her through the thin T-shirt she wore and she felt her limbs turn to cotton wool as he slowly brought his mouth close to her own. For what seemed like an age, a testing time when it seemed he was giving her the option to pull away, his lips hovered above her own. Then he must have become aware of her inability to resist and he smiled, savouring the moment, his eyes misted with the evidence of his own desire.

'So beautiful, Riva so beautiful. . .' he husked, then with toe-curling deliberation he lowered his lips on to her own, the first touch, light as it was, deepening with a sudden flare of passion that sent them both rocking ever more wildly into each other's arms as mouth sought mouth, tongue touched and answered tongue, and they became one single flame of mutual desire.

Richard was the first to break away, holding her pulsing body in his broad hands, stroking her hair with smooth, protecting caresses as if the regularity of the strokes could calm him as it was meant to calm her. She could hear the put-put of a motorboat approaching, followed by a shout as it drew near, and she wondered if this was the reason Richard was deliberately holding their sudden flare of passion in check. She was relieved, whatever the reason. Things had unexpectedly got out of hand and there was no knowing where it would have ended if they hadn't stopped then. She had been totally unprepared.

But when he spoke his words belied such thoughts as these. 'You're at a disadvantage here—I didn't intend that. I simply thought you'd like to see the boat. But you looked so beautiful.' He frowned. 'You're driving me wild, Riva. Have a heart!' He tried to speak lightly, but the look in his eyes told a different story. He pushed her gently to one side. 'Drink your coffee. I'll see who called to us out there.' He poked his head through the hatch and, while she shakily picked up a steaming mug and let her legs give way under her as she dropped down on one of the bunks, she heard him in conversation with someone evidently circling around in a motorboat.

It was a minute or two before he turned back and with a wry smile he took up a position as far away from her as he could on the opposite bunk. She closed her eyes at the reprieve, but it was short-lived for she heard a sharp exclamation then opened them to find him lowering himself beside her.

'I promise to behave,' he murmured, seeing her startled expression. 'But there's surely nothing wrong in holding you in my arms for a few minutes, is there?' Before she could answer he went on, 'It'll only be a few minutes because the lad I was just talking to wants to ask my advice about repairing one of his sails.' He put an arm round her shoulders, turning his face so that she could feel his lips against her hair.

They stayed like that, the gentle rocking of the boat lulling them into a drowsy silence. Through a porthole Riva could see a patch of blue sky, seagulls twisting in balletic aerial loops within it, their cries like the mewing of distant kittens, and just the rhythmic slapping sound of halyards against the mast to break the silence. It was strangely erotic to give herself to the gentle movements of the boat beneath them as the tide ran rapidly out to sea. Soon the anchor chain began to creak and the sound of flowing water increased.

'We ought to get ready to go back,' Richard told her, not moving, merely lifting his warm lips from the side of her face. 'The engine can wait.'

'What about your friend?' she asked, not wishing to move as the peace of being held in the protection of his embrace filled her with the sweetest lethargy.

'He can see me when we get back to shore.'

Another few minutes elapsed before he removed his arm from where it encircled her waist, but before he got up he kissed her once, warmly and deeply, breaking off before the desire he so blatantly felt could get the upper hand.

'Come on, let's go before you make me do something you regret,' he muttered. They made their way on to the deck and Riva climbed slowly down the ladder into the rowing-boat while Richard made sure all was fast on board. It had been dreamy in his arms; feelings she hadn't known existed bathed her in a soft glow. His body, warm and strong against her own, seemed to be able to tune into the secret, subtle vibrations of her own. It was magical what he could make her feel, simply by holding her.

Wrapped in each other's arms again they were soon walking back up the high street towards the office. The weather had changed with the tide and a squall of rain came down, darkening the cobblestones, making him pull her even more deeply within his protective embrace.

The shop was reasonably busy on the Saturday and Riva was glad the two girls were both in to help. They didn't seem to regard it as work and were more like two children playing shop, re-arranging the shelves, checking the price-tags, dusting and polishing, and spending hours changing the window display. It made Riva smile.

Richard must have called by the previous evening before setting off to take Ronnie to his race meeting, for there were a couple of leather-bound library books about the history of the area and a photograph album sitting on the counter when she got in at ten o'clock. The two girls were chatting about a disco they were going to that night, disappointed that they were going to be unable to drag Ronnie off with them. Riva thought about what Ronnie would be up to that night and then of him being chaperoned by Richard—and then she thought of the situation reversed. It would be impossible to imagine Richard going unnoticed. She wondered if lots of girls went to these meetings and felt sad to think they hadn't thought of inviting her along.

Saying goodnight to the girls, and that she hoped they would enjoy the disco, she went back to the cottage and had an early tea. There was a chocolate cake from the village shop as a special treat, and after she'd eaten she carried Richard's books to a comfortable corner and started to leaf through them.

The one with the name 'Crag House' tooled in gold on the spine attracted most interest for it was full of short chapters about the generations of owners who had lived there. The husband of an only daughter had been a Ravenscroft she noticed, way back in the eighteenth century, and she wondered what had happened there—the marriage had been very short-lived, the bride surviving by another sixty years, alone with her son at the Crag. But it was as if the feud between the two families had erased any references to the fate of the husband.

By nine o'clock she was tired of reading and went outside on to the quay. The evening was warm, arousing vague longings she couldn't define, and she decided to go for a walk through the little back alleys of the village before turning in.

In a few minutes she had covered every twist and turn and eventually found herself near a footbridge over the beck that flowed into the sea nearby, so she crossed it and walked along the narrow quay on the other side. There was a lifeboat shed here and she stepped over the metal runners that plunged almost vertically from the shed into the sea and gave a shudder. It would be scary enough to take the plunge from the boat-house without the added dangers of what had called the boat out. The doors had a fresh coat of paint and she wondered if the boat lying within was often put to use. After she reached the end of the quay she stood for a few moments in the warm night. It was still quite light, the sky behind her casting a pink glow over everything.

With a sigh she made her way slowly back, only pausing on the footbridge to look at the lights of the village as they started to come on one by one.

By the time she got to the other side most of the cottages on the high street had their curtains drawn. Only from the Crab and Lobster could she detect any sounds of life.

Richard was constantly on her mind.

But it wasn't until she had spread her notebooks out on the table in front of the sitting-room window with the intention of working on the lyrics of one of her songs that she saw his old car swing across her line of vision.

She opened the window. Then her hand froze on the catch. For one wild moment she had assumed he had driven down to see her. Now with a jolt she saw the real reason for his arrival.

Climbing in a leisurely way out of the car, and laughing good-humouredly down at the driver, was Linda.

She reached back inside the car and dragged out a bulging weekend bag. Tom was scrambling over the front seat and jumped down beside her. She closed the car door with a slam and, hoisting her bag over one shoulder, began to walk away from the car towards her cottage. She didn't look back and obviously expected Tom and Richard to follow. When she reached the yellow door she took out a key. Richard had Tom on his shoulders again and he strode along after her, the perfect image of a good husband and father, and went in through the garden gate. When he came up beside her he reached out and took the bag from off her shoulder. She unlocked the door and the three of them went in, Richard stooping to allow Tom to duck his head underneath the door-frame.

Happy families. Riva discovered that her hands were shaking, reflecting the turmoil in her mind. Happy families, she thought again, as if it helped to keep repeating the same phrase. No wonder he hadn't invited her along with him. Ronnie must have been dropped off at the Crag. The couple wouldn't want a kid brother around. Tom would be put to bed. . . Riva felt a metallic taste and realised she had been biting her lip so hard she had drawn blood.

She dragged herself away from the window and forced herself to go into the kitchen. Keep calm, she told herself. So what did it matter? He was nothing to her. He was simply somebody she worked with. She'd always known he was married. He had told her so himself. She clenched her fists. He had also told her it was over. He had also kissed her in a way that. . . She thumped her clenched fist on the kitchen table.

She saw too clearly the folly of trusting those bright blue eyes. Her fault. She should have known. She got up and walked about the kitchen. If it was over, why weren't they divorced? She had never asked herself that. Now she saw she had deliberately buried her head in the sand. It was obvious, it was only 'over' when it was convenient for Richard Palmer to say it was. She didn't know why Linda lived at the cottage when there was all of Crag House available. Maybe it was a trial separation. Maybe he needed his freedom? Maybe he intended to go back to Linda all along?

Suddenly she felt such a raging fury that she had allowed herself to be duped, to be charmed along into thinking—into believing—she stopped. Her mind flew to the way he had held her hand on the cliffs. 'Put your hand in mine and I will protect you.' What a laugh! If that was true—who was to protect *her* from *him*? She wanted to fly out of the house and confront him with the towering disgust she felt, but instead slumped resignedly into a kitchen chair and stared at the table.

Carefully avoiding even the most casual glance out of the windows at the front, she eventually made her way upstairs to bed. Tomorrow she would fulfil her obligations to SeaGear and nobody would ever know from looking at her how her heart had been broken.

'I won, Riva! Look!' Ronnie had brought in his trophy to show her. He sat it on her desk and folded his arms. There was a big grin on his face.

'Fantastic! That should show 'em!' she said lightly. Her voice seemed strange. 'I bet everybody was pleased with you,' she added lamely. She hung up her jacket and went briskly over to the desk. '"Under-eighteens All-Round-Champion,"' she read. 'So what did you have to do for that?' she asked, suddenly aware that Richard had come in. While Ronnie told her in exact detail how many races he'd won and what his times were and how he'd nearly bought it in the final heat, she felt Richard's presence hovering like a dark shadow. When she finally couldn't restrain herself any longer, she turned to find his eyes fastened on her face.

Ronnie at last carried his trophy back into the workroom and Richard came to stand beside her. He said, 'You were out last night, then?'

'Was I?' She lifted her head.

'There were no lights on when I came over.'

'You came over?' She couldn't stop the note of disblief in her voice. Then she pulled herself together. '*Over* from where?' she asked coolly, stressing the word over. It was obvious he wouldn't say he'd come 'over' from the Crag. 'Down, you mean, don't you? Down from the Crag?' She turned away and reached for a file. A fist slammed down on top of the file.

'What?'

When she looked up he was frowning at her. 'Do you mind, Richard?' She tugged at the file. 'If you want these export notices cleared——'

'Damn the export notices. What did you mean?'

'I was correcting your use of English——' she bit her lip '—across from somewhere on the level, down from somewhere higher up.'

'I may only read a couple of books a year, but it doesn't mean I can't say what I mean.'

'Oh?' It was her turn to frown. 'I'm sure you do—say what you mean.' She smiled. 'Now, if you wouldn't mind I'd like to get on.'

He released the file and straightened up.

'You're different this morning. What's been going on?'

It was a question Riva felt like asking too, but she rammed a piece of paper into the typewriter and rattled in the date, prepared to ignore him— but as he reluctantly turned away and reached the door of his office she couldn't resist calling, 'The break doesn't seem to have done much for your mood either. I hope everything went well.'

He swung back. 'Things went very well, as you're kind enough to ask. Yes. Extremely well. It was most productive.'

'Does enjoyment always have to be productive?' She arched her brows.

'No, Riva. . .' A smile curled his lips. 'I can think of a couple of times recently when I've indulged in totally unproductive enjoyment.' His sailor-boy eyes flicked suggestively over her face and down her body and back again. She felt as if her clothes had fallen away.

'I'm sure you have,' she replied in a voice designed to erect a wall of ice behind which she could recover.

He left her then with a small scowl and they were both busy for the rest of the morning. It was only when Richard sent Ronnie out on some errand that he came back into the office and began to prowl around as if he had something on his mind. Riva ignored him.

Eventually he came to sit on the edge of her desk. 'Riva,' he began, 'where were you last night?'

Her fingers froze over the typewriter keys. 'I don't see what my private life has to do with you.' She lifted her head and gave him a cool stare.

'Well. . .' He looked as if he violently disagreed but was striving to be reasonable about it. She watched his struggle with disbelief. His arrogance was amazing. Eventually he said, 'I suppose not. You're a free agent, after all. I just wondered.'

Wondered if there was any competition, she thought acidly. 'It's a free country, Mr Palmer. Wonder as much as you like.'

'But it's not going to get me anywhere? OK. He grinned. 'Play it that way. He doesn't seem to have put you in a very good humour, that's all. And I was just thinking, if it's anybody you want sorting out—I'm your man!'

She gave him a withering glance. '"Put your hand in mine and I will protect you"? Yes, thanks. I'll remember that. God help me if I'm ever in such dire straits.' She drowned out his reply in a gunburst of typing and when she looked up he was frowning heavily, the lips that had touched hers so traitorously compressed into a hard line. 'I don't get it,' he persisted. 'You make me feel I've done something wrong, but I can't imagine what. It's not your birthday, is it? You haven't been dropping hints about a birthday, have you?'

'Please, Richard. . .' She typed another paragraph.

'Women,' he said, still frowning. 'Life in the Navy was far simpler.' Scratching his head, he went back into the office. In a moment he called

through the open door, 'I'll take you for a sandwich at the Crab and Lobster in half an hour.
OK? And we'd better talk about time off. Your
hours are climbing sky-high.'

Yes, she thought, pretend everything's the
same, throw a few concessions my way. . .but it
won't change things now. She wanted to tell him
to search his heart for her change towards him,
but she knew there would be no point. And
anyway, he really meant nothing to her. A kiss
was a kiss. They happened all the time.

CHAPTER SEVEN

RIVA was ready for Richard when he came through as promised half an hour later. 'I'm sorry, Richard, I don't feel like the Crab and Lobster, and anyway, I've already planned what I'm having for lunch. I shall eat back at the cottage.' There was no doubt from her attitude that he was not invited. He watched her gather her things and go out without comment. As she set off down the high street she heard the shop door close behind her and guessed that he was locking up and following her down. She quickened her pace. By the time she was turning into the gate at Sea View he was directly behind her.

'Have a nice lunch,' he called as their eyes met. His own were storm-blue beneath the smile. He carried on across the road into the doorway of the pub. No doubt he'll have a suitably alcoholic meal with all his cronies, she thought, somewhat bitterly. He can't lose. Whatever happens it'll come out right. He had that look about him. As if he always came out on top.

She was busy in the kitchen with an unexciting packet of soup when she heard something come through the letter-box. It was an airmail envelope, postmarked Jamaica. She tore it open with a twinge of pleasure. It seemed ages since she'd heard anything from Dad. Scanning the first couple of paragraphs, she saw that her replacement, Miss Smithson, featured rather heavily, going under the initials DL which, she further discovered, was her father's shorthand for Dragon Lady. She smiled to herself. But before she could read any further there was a knock at the door. Too late to hide and pretend she'd gone out again, she reluctantly opened it an inch and peered out.

'Well?'

Richard stood on the path, a mug of beer in one hand and a slender glass of what looked like Bacardi and ice in the other. 'Which would you prefer?' he asked.

'How democratic. What if I choose neither?'

'Then I'm going to be ungovernably drunk this afternoon in the office. Think you can handle it?'

'Richard Palmer——' she crumpled the partially read letter into a pocket and folded her arms '—I don't see why I should be brow-beaten into——'

'Be fair! Look at it like this——' his eyes opened, wide and innocent '—it's a peace-offering for crimes unspecified. I'm not asking you to talk to me, only to accept a drink. You can't refuse that. Look,' he bent down and placed the Bacardi on the step, 'I can see you want to be alone. I'm over there if you change your mind.' He nodded towards the yard of the pub.

Leaving the drink on the step, he took his own back with him and leant on the railing outside. He hadn't been there a minute before a couple of fishermen in navy-blue sweaters and waterproof leggings came up to have a word with him. He didn't look again in the direction of Sea View. Sighing, she picked up the drink and took it indoors with her. It stood on the kitchen table for ten minutes before she relented and took a sip. He was trying to get round her—obviously—but it wouldn't work.

He called again as she was getting ready to come out. 'The landlord would like his glass back.' He stood on the doorstep, the wind ruffling his dark hair, his amazing cheekbones tightening in a smile. There was an element of caution in it. He held out one hand.

Silently she handed the glass over. He returned it across the road. By the time she had locked up he was walking up the street towards the shop. He didn't wait for her and was already in his office when she let herself in. He came through though, as soon as he heard the door, emerging suddenly from around a rack of wet suits, his manner businesslike.

'When do you want to take your days off? Have you thought about it?'

'I thought I was supposed to have Tuesdays off. It's only Sunday today.' She came to a stop a good three feet away.

'You missed last week. Didn't you work right through?'

She nodded.

'You're owed time off, then. Take tomorrow as

well as Tuesday. And listen, you've been here a month or more so what about a pay review?'

She shrugged.

He named a figure that was a third higher than what she was getting.

'Fine, thanks. . . If you think you can afford it,' she added without thinking.

'Don't be funny. You've seen the books. You're worth your weight. And you'll get more if you stay. I was more than half serious when I suggested making you a director, Riva.'

She raised her head. 'Richard, you don't have to do this.' She squared her shoulders and went to walk past him, but he stepped sideways, barring her way.

'Do what? Offer you fair terms of employment?'

'Appease me or whatever it is you think you're doing.'

He looked surprised. 'Why should I want to appease you?'

She felt her throat tighten in anger. 'You know damn well why. Now move out of my way!' She tried to push past him, but it was a mistake as she realised almost as soon as she made a move for his hands came out, grabbing her by the upper arms.

'Not so fast. There's something going on here. What is it?'

She raised eyes that were now glistening with pent-up misery. 'You lied to me, Richard. You lied about your relationship with your wife. You lied to me all along. As it happens, I don't care a damn. It's just that I don't like being made to look a fool. Now will you let go?'

'No, I will not.' He pulled her closer and one hand cupped her chin so he could look into her face. 'What is all this?' he rasped. 'When have I lied to you? What have I lied about, for heaven's sake? You know I'm still legally married. You've known all along. So what's the big deal?'

His blue eyes roamed her face as if to glean every ounce of informatoin from its changing colour. Riva felt her mind go blank as his body came up hotly against her own. She felt the familiar weakening sensation in her legs. With a spurt of energy she twisted out of his grasp and stepped back, colliding with the rack of wet suits. They swung violently and Richard's hands groped among them to steady them. The smell of new rubber enveloped her and then it mingled again with the warm spice-scent of limes as he reached out for her.

She slipped into his arms before she could stop herself and he put her head on his shoulder, stroking it with tender strokes, fingers running over and over through the blonde strands of her hair. 'I knew there was something. But why now, love? You know about Linda. You've always known. I know it makes a difference for you and I haven't tried to pressure you. I thought I was behaving with unbelievable self-control. Soon it's all going to change, you'll see. . .'

His murmuring voice began to work on her so

that, overcome to the point where she knew she was likely to give in, she would listen to everything he had to tell her. She struggled out of his reach again, confusion plain to see in her eyes.

'I don't want to hear about her. I've already told you, how you manage your life is your concern. If you want to live in separate houses, fine. You don't owe me an explanation. But don't tell me lies. And don't make lying promises about how things are going to change because I won't listen. I saw you bringing her back last night. I'm not blind and I'm not stupid either. I know you spent Friday night together——'

'So *that's* it.' His face had gone cold.

He's going to try and talk his way out of it, she thought as he stepped forward, his eyes as soulless and innocent as the ocean. 'Don't waste your time,' she clipped. 'Why the hell should you think I care a solitary damn?'

She pivoted, but again he put out a hand. This time there was no tenderness in it.

'You will listen!' he said through clenched teeth. 'And sure—I spent the night with my wife and son. We stayed with one of my sisters. A nice, happy family crowd. But I didn't sleep with her, Riva. We don't do that any more. Believe me.'

'Of course I believe you,' she said sarcastically. 'Why ever would you lie about a thing like that?'

He closed his eyes as if trying to focus on something, but she went on relentlessly, 'If your marriage is really on the rocks as you say, why haven't you had a divorce? That's what most people do. Or is there some special reason against that too?' Her fists were bunched by her sides. 'Now you'll try to tell me there's some good, convenient reason for keeping it going——' Suddenly tears of anger filled her eyes and she dashed them away, turning for escape towards the back room.

'Riva—listen, truly——' He paused, raising a hand, but letting it drop when he saw her face. 'There has never seemed to be any urgency about divorce. It won't make a scrap of difference to anything. I support Linda and my son. The courts aren't going to give her a better deal and she knows it. She's got nothing to gain by divorce. It doesn't matter one way or the other. The only time it would make any difference to the way things are is if either of us decides to get married again. Until now,' he went on, 'that's been the last thing on my mind. . .'

'Good. I hope you won't let anything change the situation. With your record you're obviously best out of the marriage market!' She fled into the next room and slammed the door. He didn't follow and she looked round the small office with a trapped look. There was no point in staying here and trying to work. The place wasn't big enough for them both.

A tiny clear core of common sense pushed its way through the turmoil of emotion, making her review her afternoon's work. There was nothing she couldn't do in the safety of Sea View. She snatched up the appropriate files and went to the door. Richard was standing in the window of the shop looking out at the street with his thumbs looped in the leather belt of his 501s. He didn't raise his head.

She said. 'I'm taking some work home. I'll drop it in on my way past tomorrow. Then I'm going to take two days off, as we agreed. I'll be back on Wednesday morning.' Without waiting for his reply, she went out.

When she got back to the cottage she made herself a hot drink, dragged a blanket off the spare bed and lay curled up in one of the armchairs, her mind stuck in one groove. He had lied and now he'd tried to wriggle out of it. Only a fool would believe a man like him. What else would he say, for goodness' sake? That yes, he *had* slept with his wife? It was laughable. *She* was laughable— for even half believing he was telling the truth. Was it *likely*?

She got up after half an hour and tidied herself up, folded the blanket and put it back on the bed. Then she went downstairs, opened the files and polished off the necessary work in half the time she'd expected. Then, remembering the letter from her father, she took that out and read it twice. He seemed to have adapted to the regimen of Miss Smithson with remarkable enthusiasm. But he still wrote as if he expected her to return at any moment. Well, maybe she would. It hadn't been such a brilliant idea, playing Cinderella in reverse. It had been no fun at all. She would do what she had been taught to do when things got heavy—move on out. That was what she would do now, when the first chance came up.

There was a postscript to the letter, scribbled on the back of one of the pages where she hadn't noticed it. 'Heard from Marl just now—he wants to place a couple of your songs and asks for more. Ring me when we return to Ocho Rios end June.'

She frowned. That was three weeks away. He wasn't working if he was away from base for so long. Still that was his affair. But it was annoying to be left up in the air like this. Did Marl, her father's agent, mean he could actually sell some of her songs? She felt a quickening of excitement. Despite paternal encouragement, she had kept them much to herself so far, not feeling confident enough to let them take their chance in the outside world. It was naughty of Dad to show them to anyone else—but she knew he wouldn't have done it if he had felt they would shame her.

The news acted like a tonic and she spent the rest of the evening working on the ones she had with her and sketching out a few ideas for new ones. Richard Palmer could go jump in a lake.

Next morning she was up at six. It wasn't only the good news from Jamaica sending out alarms, it was the need to escape from Scarswick before Richard was out and about. After leaving the completed file in the empty shop, she had to walk right up past the end of the drive leading to the Crag. Any minute she expected to hear Richard's shout behind her. But she made it unobserved to the car park at the top end and was soon driving on to the moor road. She didn't have any particular destination in mind and didn't want one. It was a pattern she was used to—this was what Dad would do when he got fed up. 'Let's hit the road, kid,' he would say, adopting an American accent, and they would drive and drive, the radio on, the windows down, the open road before them.

With enough miles between her and Richard Palmer she would soon begin to see the whole thing as the sorry escapade it was. She started to sing, remembering a phrase young Tom had used in his excitement at being taken out into the bay— 'Let's punch on down, Dad!' She began to weave it into a song. 'Let's punch on down the highway. . .' Any highway is the right highway, she told herself, so long as it leads away from Richard Palmer.

She drove up to Durham to look at the cathedral and spent the night at a small inn. The next day she thought she'd pay a visit to Hadrian's wall, and spent the best part of the day in the car, as it was further away than she'd allowed for. That meant she had to drive through the night to reach Scarswick in time for work on the Wednesday morning.

It was three o'clock when she finally drove down the village street. Nothing would have induced her to leave the car at the top as she would have had to trudge nearly a quarter of a mile in the pitch-dark to the bottom end. This way she simply had to park and cross the staithe.

She was just inserting the key in the front door when a movement over by the harbour wall set her nerves jangling. As she threw a hasty glance over her shoulder, a dark shape detached itself and stepped forward into the moonlight. The key clattered to the step. 'What are you doing here?' she croaked.

Richard, wearing a navy-blue polo-necked fisherman's sweater, seemed to glide over the cobblestones like a ghost. When he reached the gate he came to an abrupt halt. 'Where the hell have you been?' he called, keeping his voice low. 'If you hadn't left your things all over the cottage I'd've assumed you'd done a bunk. I thought——' He ran a hand through his cropped hair in a familiar gesture, then, coming to a decision, he slammed the garden gate back on its hinges and covered the few feet up the path before Riva could blink. He wrapped his arms round her and squeezed her against him, his hands rough as they kneaded her soft-as-putty limbs to the shape of his own hard body.

'Riva, Riva, Riva,' he muttered. 'I imagined you upside-down in some ditch in the mangled wreckage of your car. I didn't know how to stop thinking it. Why didn't you ring or something? You could've told me where you were going. Hell, Riva, never leave me like that again. You know better than to walk out on a quarrel, don't you? Was it deliberate? A deliberate torture? Please, baby. . .' His two hands were on either side of her face and he turned it up to him, eyes glittering in the dark, his whole face tight with the tension of his emotions.

She was astonished, first by his sudden appearance out of the dark, and second by this blatant show of feeling when she had spent the last two days convincing herself that she meant no more to him than simply another notch on the bedpost. She felt the tell-tale response as her body recognised his need and echoed it.

'I've dropped my key,' she muttered, scraping about with one of her feet to find it in the dark. He slithered his hands down her body as if about to release her, then, changing his mind, dragged her hard up against him, bringing his lips down at the same time so that her body arched in his arms, her mouth suddenly the recipient of the touch she had been dreaming of ever since she'd left.

When he released her he was breathing heavily. He put one hand on the wall beside her head as if to steady himself. 'Why did you do it? Why, Riva?'

'I——' She put up a hand to her throbbing lips. 'What have I done? I told you I was going away. . .'

'Just as I told you—oh, never mind. We don't trust each other an inch, do we? Look, can we go inside?'

'I'm not sure that would be wise——'

'I promise I won't touch you. . .unless you ask me to,' he added with a half-hearted attempt at a smile. 'Come on, we can't stand out here all night. I've been sitting on that wall for hours.'

Her lips had gone dry and she licked them, tasting the salt from his skin with a shock or recognition. 'I dropped the key when you pounced out of the dark like that,' she told him. 'Help me find it.'

Together they crouched down on the step, the warmth of Richard's hand as it accidentally touched hers making her draw back with an almost audible gasp. When they straightened, the key at last in his hand, she asked, 'Can I trust you to—well, to behave properly?'

'We've got to learn to trust each other,' he replied. 'We'd better start as soon as possible.'

She let him put the key in the lock and waited until he reached inside and switched on the light before she stepped in after him. Once inside he pressed the key into her hands.

She put it back in the lock and went through into the kitchen, keeping her coat on and switching on the wall heater. The place felt cold now and she put the kettle on, remaining by the hob as if it would stop the shivering that was suddenly affecting her.

He came up behind her and wrapped his arms round her as if to warm her, but she pulled away. 'You promised.'

He released her at once. 'OK.' He straddled a wooden chair. 'How do we start to sort out all the misunderstandings between us, Riva? Where do we begin?'

She stood silent, willing the kettle to boil so she would have something to do that would release the dreadful tension his presence was creating in some deep place within her. She still hadn't got over the shock of his sudden appearance. It was something she couldn't account for. 'What were you really doing out here at this time of night?' she asked, forcing herself to speak, eyes assessing every turn and twist of his head as if to judge the truth of his reply.

He closed his eyes, his tanned face haggard in the overhead light. 'Can you believe I was waiting for you?' He opened them, an endless ocean of blue, and looked full into her own. 'I expected to see you back around teatime. Or some time in the evening. Or, when you hadn't shown up then, some time before midnight. When it got to be one in the morning I began to think I was going mad. I'm sorry if that seems,' he searched around for a word, 'possessive. . .' He gave a harsh laugh. 'I am possessive. Riva,' his voice roughened, 'you know what I'm trying to say. I want you. I can't let you go. These last two days without you have made me see that. You're mine. You have to be.' She saw how white his knuckles were as they gripped the back of the chair.

'*Yours*, Richard? How *can* I be yours?' Her lip curled. She didn't doubt the sincerity of his feelings, now, looking at him, with every line of his face marked with the force of them, but they were misplaced if he truly thought he had a right to say such things to her in his situation.

'Let me tell you about Linda and me——'

'No!' She turned, hands to her ears. 'I don't want to hear!'

His chair scraped as he rose to his feet. She felt his hands come up over her own, pulling them down, forcing her to listen. 'You're going to listen and you're going to listen well.'

'No, you can't make me! I know what you'll try to do!' She spun to face him. 'You'll tell me some story that makes it all sound plausible and—and——'

'And what, Riva? What are you so afraid of? You think I'll spin you a yarn just to get you into bed for the night? What would happen next morning? Wouldn't the truth come out?'

'It'd be too late then, wouldn't it?' she replied in a tight voice.

'My God, you must have known some complete——' He broke off, running both hands through his hair and going back to the wooden chair, flinging himself down in it with a frustrated curse. 'Listen to me, Riva, I don't care a damn what sort of man you're used to,' his glance trailed over her body like smoke, 'but do me a favour, will you? Look at *me*. Maybe we all claim we're different—I wouldn't know. But I can tell you one thing without any doubt—I won't lie to you, ever. And if that makes me different from the others then so be it.'

'You're not different, Richard. I understand they all claim to tell God's honest truth.'

'I can't win, can I?' He tilted his head and

looked up at the ceiling. The kitchen was filling with steam. 'Kettle,' he suggested. And when she didn't move at once he got to his feet, switched it off then looked round. 'What did you intend? Hot water?'

'No—I—there's some tea——'

But he was already rummaging around in the cupboard and, coming up with a packet, he held it up. 'Cup-a-Soup? Why not?' He took down two mugs and poured an equal measure of powder into each, adding water, stirring them both, then handing one to Riva. 'Can't we sit somewhere more comfortable than this?' Without waiting for a reply, he went into the sitting-room. By the time she followed he was piling sticks in the grate. He turned to her. 'Matches?'

'Really, it's a waste of time——'

'You mean you think I'm going to drink my soup and make polite small talk then go away like a good boy five minutes later? Could you sleep, Riva, with all this hanging unresolved over our heads? I want the slate cleared. When I walk out of that front door we're both going to know exactly where we stand. If,' his voice softened, 'if I'm to leave for the last time, then it's going to be unequivocal. Do you understand?'

'Don't threaten me!' she burst out. 'Go now and save yourself some trouble.'

'I don't want to go.' His voice lowered and he crouched on the rug in front of the fire looking up at her, his eyes bright with feeling. 'I know part of you wants to see the back of me. But another part of you wants me to stay—maybe a very long time. . .' He stretched out a hand and touched the back of hers as it held the mug. 'Let's talk?'

She moved out of reach and went to stand with the sofa between them. He'd got the fire to blaze up nicely already. She watched as he started to put pieces of coal on it, one by one, paying careful attention to what he was doing. His hands were large and long-fingered, caressing hands, dependable hands. She wondered if they could tell as much about a man as it seemed they could, looking at his. She turned away. She was doing his job for him, seducing herself with crazy speculations about what his hands would feel like, running free over her naked body.

'God, this is impossible!' She burst out, spinning away and pacing about the room and finally going to perch on the window-seat as far away from him as she could get. 'It's nearly four in the morning. And I'm dog-tired. What can you possibly say that's of any interest? What line are you going to take, Richard? Get to the point. What do you imagine is the right approach for me?'

He straightened. 'This isn't a game, Riva. I'm not interested in pressing the right button to hit the jackpot. All I want is that you should know the facts so you can make up your own mind about us. If you still feel it's no go,' he shrugged and his jaw clenched, 'I guess I'll abide by that decision.' He sat on the arm of a chair. 'You're going to sit over there, are you? It's much warmer by the fire.'

'It'll soon warm up. It's only a small room,' she replied, burying her face in her mug.

'You may remember when we had that argument over Ronnie,' he began, stretching out his legs to the fire. He had left his rubber boots near the door and was wearing a pair of thick grey sea socks. He rested them on the fender as if he were in his own home. 'I said something you wanted to take up, but——' he tightened his lips '—I fobbed you off. I shouldn't have. But I did. It seemed too soon to start telling you about my misspent youth. What I'd said was that I didn't want Ronnie making the same mistake as me. Quite rightly you wanted to know what I meant.'

She remembered it now. It had been the time he had kissed her at the Crag.

'The thing is, I guess I was much like Ronnie at his age. Oh, I didn't steal cars and wreck them— Dad saw I never went that far. But I was a little wild. My mates were the lads off the boats when I was home from school. They were a pretty wild bunch, though you might not think so to look at them now they're all married with families. . .boating parties of tourists around the bay every summer!'

Riva sighed. He heard the sound and looked across. 'Don't musunderstand, I'm not making excuses. I don't regret a damned thing. What I'm saying is, running with a crowd like that, I got involved with the sister of one of them. She was——' he bit his lip '—sixteen? I was twenty. Old enough to know better. But,' he smiled resignedly, 'fate takes a hand now and then and we were the unlucky ones in the lottery. It brought me down to earth with a thud, I can tell you. Neither of us wanted to marry, but her father turned up at the Crag with a shot-gun. I reckon he meant to use it as well. But Dad was on his side. "He's made his bed, now the young devil's got to lie in it," he said. Quite right too. I couldn't have walked out on her. We married in the village church. She in white. And eight months later Tom was born.

'I'd already been accepted into the navy and Linda was brought up in a sea-faring family so she never expected me to stay on shore for long. It could have worked. I've seen marriages like that work. If we'd been able to share other things, not just sex——' He shrugged. 'But our backgrounds were very different. We had very little in common. I was an officer. And she hated all the protocol. The formal dinners. The other wives!'

He laughed. 'She came out on a couple of foreign postings with me, but hated it. Made no attempt to fit in. She couldn't wait to be back home with her family. She wouldn't adapt.'

His eyes closed, the short, thick lashes resting lightly on his cheek. 'Things just got out of hand after that. When we met, which wasn't often, we fought. It was a living hell. It began to affect Tom. I just spent as much time away as I could. Then Dad died, things changed here, Ronnie started to get into trouble. I didn't want to come back. I had a good career. The sky was the limit. And what was there for me here? Linda and I had long ago stopped trying to keep up a pretence for Tom. We were unable to adjust in any way to each other's needs. Then there was the Crag falling down around my ears. The trouble was, there was no choice. I had to come back.'

He gave the fire another shovel of coal and went on, 'She's had her men-friends. Shore wives. They know what their husbands get up to, I suppose. That's how it goes. That's the sort of life you expect under those conditions. We accept that as part of the package.'

He opened his eyes and looked straight at her. 'I've done a lot of thinking about the kind of life I would really have, given a free rein, and it's not that sort, Riva.'

He suddenly sat up. 'Did you look at those books I brought down from the library for you?'

Startled by his change of tack, she nodded.

'Read the one about one of your distant uncles?'

'The one who married Isabel Palmer?'

He chuckled. 'A rare devil he was, one of the biggest smugglers around. Whether or not Isabel was simply hoping to control the Ravenscroft empire by marrying into it, who knows? But I rather doubt that was the whole story. It seems rather tragic.' He was looking into the fire now. 'Just a week after they were married,' he told her, 'Daniel Ravenscroft was drowned. Your family's version is that a ship went down off the headland and he went out to save lives, but lost his own in the process. The Palmer version is that he went out to see what he could loot from the sinking ship. We'll never know the truth. but what we do know is that Isabel never remarried, and her reputation was such that she was called the Bride of Ravenscroft for the rest of her life. That, Riva,' he said, his eyes dwelling on her upturned face, 'is the kind of fidelity I can understand.'

CHAPTER EIGHT

IT WAS an hour after dawn when Richard made a move to leave Sea View. Riva got up, yawning drowsily, her hair tumbling in disarray about her shoulders. True to his word he had behaved perfectly and, when it seemed pointless to remain aloof any longer, she had snuggled up beside him on the sofa in front of the fire, feeling his strong arms protectively enclosing her with a deep sense of contentment.

He held her in his arms before he left, his face resting against hers. 'I'd better go before people start getting about. In a place like this your reputation will be shot to pieces if anybody sees me leaving at this time in the morning.'

'What will happen when Linda finds out?' she asked, anxious for reassurance.

'All hell will break loose!'

'But you said——' Her startled glance made him laugh.

'She's got a chap of her own these days. I'm only surprised she hasn't sent me the divorce papers already. No doubt, like me, she simply hasn't got around to it.' He held her close. 'That'll be my first job this morning, Riva. I never really appreciated how unfair on you it was.' He kissed her then, drawing from her a hint of the loving

she so desperately wanted to give. Then he went
to the door, pushing his feet into his boots and
opening the door to look out.

'It's a lovely day,' she breathed, coming up
beside him and resting her head on his shoulder.
The sky was ice-blue. Seagulls were flung up into
it like scraps of white paper.

He looked across at her car parked near the
harbour wall. 'First thing you do this morning is
move your car up to the top,' he told her.

'I may do——'

'Riva, I'm not suggesting, I'm insisting. Do it,
OK?'

'But why? It's not in the way there—'

'If this wind freshens we'll be getting some
heavy seas. With a high tide as well it could get
hairy. OK?'

'Oh, all right, Richard. You're not in the Navy
now, you know!'

'You'd be court-martialled soon as look at you
if I were! You look as if you have only one
function in life. . .' He pulled her fiercely into his
arms and gave her another lingering kiss. 'Soon
you're going to come up to the Crag to have a
look at my paintings,' he warned her with a
wicked smile. 'In fact, name the day, I'm always
available. . .'

'I bet you are.' She snuggled against him.

'For you. Only for you.' He brushed the top of
her head with his lips. 'Let me go before——'

'Before the golden coach turns back into a
pumpkin?' she smiled, remembering something

about Cinderella that had been on her mind in another life.

'Before it's too late,' he amended. 'I'm human, not super-human, as you seem to think. There are limits to my self-control.' As if to prove what he was saying his hands slipped underneath her sweater and she undulated against him with a small gasp of pleasure. It was with an effort that she forced herself to move away.

'Richard, I do want—I. . .' She was lost for words, just looking at him, his tough face and devastating smile making her heart do somersaults.

'We both want. And we're both going to get what we want.' He brought her roughly into his arms one last time, then turned to go. 'Don't forget your car.'

Then he was gone. Riva leaned against the door-frame for long moments after he turned the corner and disappeared up the high street. She had started out a few hours ago determined he could say nothing to make her change her mind about him. But somehow, without seeming to try, simply by telling her frankly how he had got into marriage and what it had been like, he had converted her into a true believer. She wondered now how she could ever have doubted him. Those honest eyes, blue as innocence, beguiled her heart and she willingly handed it over to him, trusting he would look after it, making things work out for them both.

She was about to turn back inside when a small

figure from further down the quay shot out of one of the cottages. It was Tom. He ran up to her gate, pausing uncertainly, then in a rush he demanded, 'Was that my dad?'

Riva nodded. Without a word the boy dashed off up the street. She bit her lip, but restrained herself from going after him.

Tom's sudden appearance was the one shadow over what had been a morning of fragile joy. Everything seemed new, as if touched by a magic paintbrush, bringing unexpected colour to what had previously seemed dull and commonplace. She guessed it was love. It was being in love. She cherished it, knowing from hearsay that it was something precious.

When she went into the shop Ronnie was working by himself. 'Richard's gone off to Scarborough,' he informed her. 'I don't know how he's got the energy.' He gave her a sidelong glance.

'What *can* you mean, Ronnie?' Riva busied herself with routine correspondence and ignored the knowing glint in his eye. He was impossible for seventeen. Lord knew what Richard had been like at that age and later at twenty. No wonder the sixteen-year-old Linda had been unable to resist him!

As before, he was right about the weather. Riva went through into the shop and didn't need to think twice about whether to open up or not. It was almost pitch-dark, though only mid-morning.

After lunch rain began to lash against the plate glass and soon the sloping cobbled street was running with water. She expected the sky to lighten after the cloudburst, but it didn't and the rain continued.

From the back room she could hear Ronnie hard at work. He was whistling between his teeth. Eventually the sound began to get on her nerves. Richard was being far longer than she'd expected. Doubt and fears, exacerbated by the malevolent weather, sent her aimlessly back and forth from office to shop, unable to settle to anything. At long last she heard the door open. He was there, looking like an advert for pipe tobacco, wearing yellow oilskins, rain slicking his hair, making it curl, just like that first time she had set eyes on him. It seemed an age ago.

'Not too good out there. Did you bring a waterproof with you?' He took her straight into his arms. She shook her head, concerned only to feel the reassurance of his body at long last against her own, feeling the heat of him as he held her inside the opening of his topcoat. Drips of water scattered around them.

'You're going to get even wetter out there, my lovely,' he murmured, nuzzling her neck. His lips closed over her own, cold and tasting of rain, taking her warmth, returning it, melting with hers in shared exchange. He lifted his head. 'I don't suppose you put the shutters up at Sea View, did you?'

'I didn't think——'

'It's going to get worse. Let's go back and do it now.'

She shivered. She could tell from the way he kissed her that it would lead further. For a moment she hesitated and he saw it in her eyes. 'I saw my solicitor,' he told her. 'Everything's going to be all right. It's a formality after so many years apart. They call it desertion.' He gave an ironic laugh. 'I'm not sure who deserted whom. It'd be more appropriate to call it drifting.'

'I can't imagine you drifting in or out of anything, Richard. You're so positive.'

'Let's say my attention was elsewhere at the time. Linda's certainly was.' He scowled. 'I hope. . .'

'What do you hope?' she prompted.

'I hope we're not going to let it overshadow what we have. . .?' He took both her hands in his and held them close to his lips. 'It all seemed to take place in another world. If it weren't for Tom there would only be a distant bitter-sweet memory. . .I don't intend to make the same mistake twice, Riva. Trust me.' Then he bent his head and she felt the flooding warmth of his lips on the backs of her hands.

He insisted she put on his oilskin jacket and pull up the hood, telling her that his sweater was oiled wool and would keep off the worst of the weather if they hurried. Then they told Ronnie where they were going before plunging out into the rain.

The force of the wind took Riva's breath away,

then one of Richard's arms came round her shoulders dragging her along beside him. It seemed quieter down on the quayside and there were no waves crashing against the harbour wall as there had been a week ago. When she said as much he grunted something about low tide then bundled her indoors. 'If the wind drops before the tide comes in you'll be all right down here. If not, well, we'll keep an eye on things.'

She hung his yellow jacket on the peg in the entrance where it began to drip water over the red tiles, but he took it down at once. 'I'll go out and fix the shutters.'

When he came back in she was waiting for the kettle to boil. It was strange in the front sitting-room with the wooden shutters over the windows, but there was light of a sort in the back kitchen, though filtered by the rain that was streaming down the windows as if the cottage itself had taken to the seas. She reached out to put the electric heater on, but nothing happened and she tapped it impatiently. Richard flicked the light switch on, then off.

'Your electricity's gone,' he told her. 'It must be quite bad further up the coast.' She was shivering. He reached out and pulled her into his arms. She could hear the thump of his heart against her ribs and for a while he simply held her in his arms, close and protected, like something precious. Then she felt him move, his body alive with need. He tilted her face to his. 'Yes,' he told her as if she had asked a question. 'Yes,

now. . .now, my love. . .we can't pretend any
longer.'

Her limbs were unresisting as he picked her up
in his arms and carried her out of the room to the
narrow stairs. The little bedroom at the back was
almost in darkness. Rain drummed on the
window. He placed her on the bed, bending
beside it to reach for her shoes. He slipped them
off, fondling her bare feet with his sure touch.
Then while she lay still, heart racing, mind a
turmoil of wanting and fearing what she wanted,
the giving that would be all she had to give, she
felt him reach up for her, loosening her belt from
around her slim waist, thrusting it to the floor
beside the bed. The gesture was like reaching a
stage on a journey, the destination of which they
both knew.

She had time to draw back, but her limbs lay
melting in pools of expectation, waiting for where
he chose to take her next. His eyes raked her slim
form, then he reached for her blouse, each button
opening at his touch, from the top one to the
bottom, his fingers moving with deliberation,
building the tension. He paused when he had
finished, giving her a moment's respite when she
felt he might turn back, change his mind, stop,
anything—but his eyes were worshipping the
golden V of skin revealed in the opening of her
blouse while she lay still, trembling as if at a
physical touch as his eyes explored her quivering
shape.

'I've longed to touch you, to glory in your sweet

womanhood, Riva. I want to love you, and lie with you, to be sated with you, to possess you entirely.' His eyes softened, glowing dark with desire, and she felt his weight settle beside her on the bed, the fingers of one hand beginning to trace an arousing pattern over her skin.

Then his dark head came down, pressuring softly over her breasts, touching the peaks to the trembling start of a new desire. She gave a sigh, her limbs, soft and yielding till now, tensing with awakened need. She forced her arms around his neck, bringing her fingers running lightly through his strong, dark hair, then she found his shoulders, her hands feathering exploratively down the broad back, pulling at his shirt, suddenly quickening their movements, grappling with the restrictions of garments as she began to twist and turn beneath him.

He fought with the fasteners on her waistband, ripping the skirt down over her hips, squeezing her soft flesh in ever more rapid signs of his increasing desire. She squirmed to free her shoulders from her blouse then rose to meet him, joying in the feel of his rough chest against her own skin, shivering and pulsing as he closed with her in an ecstatic coming together that made her cry his name out loud. Then he paused, his self-control hanging by a thread. 'Riva. . .?'

'It's all right. . .' she husked, head flung back as she lifted her aching body, inviting him to take it in its deepest embrace. Her whispered invocation broke the ragged sound of their breathing as she demanded, 'Yes, Richard, yes. . .possess me. . .take me. . .' Then sweet fire flooded over her as he plunged into her secret depths, his movements savage and tender, drawing her on into a maelstrom of desire, taunting her to the edge of fulfilment, drawing back from the brink again and again, then taking her spiralling sensations down, deeper into herself, to horizons she had never imagined, where his body became part of her own and the two of them soared free of boundaries like two gulls loosed into the sky, until the joy of ultimate union washed over them, bringing them gasping to a state of peace.

His weight, his hot, filmy skin heating her own, heightened every sensation. Her eyes opened, her tongue darting out at the same moment to lick the hard curve of his cheek, slithering over the rough silk of his skin, making his lips move in a search for contact with her own. He pulled the duvet over their heads, shutting them into the warm dark, all the cold and the rain and the heightening moan of the wind over the rooftop held at a comfortable distance.

'Shall we stay here forever?' he murmured, tasting the hair at her temple, letting his own lips pulse in time with the beating of it under the fragile skin.

'For the rest of the day, all night, yes. . .'

'You're so lovely, Riva—perhaps I'm supposed to say that first? Exquisite golden goddess. . .I never knew you could get such a tan in London.' He kissed her lightly on the nose as if to take any sting out of the words. She felt him wait, pattering light kisses over her neck, one hand again cupping a breast.

She knew what was in his mind, the unspoken question. With a tightening in her throat she began, 'You saw me get an airmail letter the other day, didn't you?'

She felt his weight shift. His eyes were inches from her own, alert now, blue and amethyst flecked cobalt.

'It was from Jamaica. I—I've spent some time there,' she admitted. 'It's still true about London. There is a flat in Knightsbridge. I was going back there to find a job. Then I came here and—I was just passing through. . .'

'Passing through on your way to somewhere else. . .just passing through?'

Her fingers plaited the short crop of dark hair at his nape. 'I seem to have stayed longer than I intended. . .'

'And Jamaica? Are you going back?'

'I expect so. . .'

'I thought it was my out-of-date marriage that was keeping us apart.' He propped himself on one arm and she saw he was frowning. His free hand came down, raking possessively through the long strands of blonde hair. His mouth lowered to her breasts, kissing them suddenly in a fever of insatiable need. She felt her eyes close with reawakening desire, but the urgency of his response brought her hands hard against the corded muscles, steadying him, one hand pushing at his mouth, to still him in his sudden fever. She tried to drag his head up to look at her, to pay attention to what she wanted to say. His expression was difficult to see in the darkness of the room with the duvet shrouded over them where he had pulled it to keep out the cold, but she could feel his eyes licking over her face.

'Richard——' she began.

Then her eyes widened as a siren split their ears. He jerked over her, his hands on either side of her head, his body taut. His eyes closed as if to shut out the sound that was shrieking through the room.

'Hell, I've got to go. Where are my things?' He pulled himself out of her embrace, reaching for his scattered clothing in the same movement. She watched in astonishment as he pulled his shirt on, ripped the oiled sweater over his head, feverishly searching for underpants and the tracksuit he had had on under his oilskins.

'Richard, what is it?'

'The lifeboat,' he muttered, dragging on his socks. 'Distress call.' He was fully clothed in a moment. The wind battered against the roof and Riva automatically pulled the duvet closer around her naked body, the siren sound chilling her as much as the cold.

He was at the door by now and paused. 'Good timing, huh?' There was something bleak in his eyes as he looked down at her golden form amid the white sheets. 'It was great, Riva. Thanks a lot. Don't forget to send me a postcard if you leave before I get back.' With that he was gone. She heard him clatter down the stairs and after a second in which she only had time to reach the bedroom door he was out, the slamming door telling her he had gone.

She ran to the front bedroom then remembered the shutters were across. Swearing softly, she stood on the landing, hugging the duvet around her shivering body. It was pointless to try to watch him go. He had told her clearly what he was going to do.

The siren was slowing down now, dropping a tone, dying, dwindling down the minor scale till it finally bleated to a halt. The silence that followed was almost more nerve-racking than the piercing screech of it. Except that it wasn't silence—not with the wind crashing ever more loudly around the rooftops.

Too frightened to get back into bed, she groped in the semi-darkness for her own clothes and made her way downstairs. The light outside was failing rapidly and she went into the kitchen to search out some candles. When she was sure she had some form of light for later on she went to the front door and forced it open. The wind was howling like a monster, bringing the sea in a constant surge against the top of the wall. The tide had turned, but as Richard had feared the wind had risen and now the two in combination were creating a hell of wind and water in the bay, spilling in fury against the rocky shore as if trying to grip the land itself in its tentacles.

Her teeth clenched as she thought of the life-boat putting out in this. With a whimper of fear she dragged on her own flimsy raincoat and a pair of gumboots and hurried out into the storm. She had to lean against the wind to make any sort of progress as it snatched and buffeted at her as if trying to pluck her from the ground itself. She reached the wall, hanging tightly on to the railings, and tried to see across the heaving waters to the other side towards the lifeboat station. But it was too far back in the haven behind the village, and the water was too turbulent to enable any sort of shape to be discerned among its mountainous peaks.

Thoroughly drenched in the couple of minutes it had taken to cross the staithe, she hurried back inside the cottage, pushing the door shut against the deafening roar outside. There was nothing to do but wait. But for how long? She went into the kitchen and lit a couple of candles, then sat huddled inside her coat, trying to steady the rising hysteria of her fears.

Relentlessly, Richard's last words came back, harrowing through her with the bitter steel of recrimination. He seemed to think she could make love like that then walk out with no more feeling than a fish. Passing through, he had said. He had looked so cold when he left. Yet he couldn't believe that was her nature. The shakiness of her emotions sent her thoughts in all directions, convincing her one minute that he wanted her to leave, and the next, making her remember the heaven of his touch, the gentleness in his eyes as he had taken her to him.

An extra hammering on the door brought her out of the half-frozen state she was sinking into, and with stiff limbs she picked up a candle and went to answer it. She knew it couldn't be Richard, for he would have come straight in. The wind at once blew out the candle flame as the door swung open.

A man's voice said, 'I thought there was somebody in here. Come on up to top, lass. The sea wall's going to go.'

'What?' Bleary-eyed, she peered into the darkness. An old man in a sou' wester stood on the path. It was already covered by a dark tide of water and the man turned back to the gate.

'Get yourself up to the chapel. The women are laying on hot drinks and bedding. Happen you'll be spending the night up there. Come on, get a move on. No time to lose!' She saw him splash through the black waters to the row of cottages further down.

Like an automaton Riva pulled on her raincoat. It was almost totally useless and felt soggy even as it closed around her shoulders, but it would have to do. The minute she stepped outside and closed the door she felt water slop over the top of her boots. It was rising silently now and with sinister rapidity across the road and into the gardens of the houses. A group of huddled shapes splashed past, their torches picking out the way it was lapping against the walls of the houses. Following in their wake, she realised that one of the group was young Tom. Linda must be among those other hurrying shapes.

One of them turned as soon as the group reached the relative dry land of the cobbled street, noticing her and calling out, 'All right? You'd better come with us!'

They waited until she caught up with them. 'With a bit of luck it'll hold,' an elderly woman said, 'but better to be safe than sorry. Did you have time to put any sandbags over your front door, love?' she asked Riva.

'I didn't know it was going to be as bad as this. Is that what you're supposed to do, then?'

'You're in that holiday cottage, are you?' The woman fell into step beside her. Riva was conscious that Tom was tugging at the arm of a woman in front. He said something and she turned, face hidden beneath a hood.

'Yes,' she forced herself to reply.

'Just here for a few weeks, then. It's not exactly holiday weather for you!' One or two of them laughed sympathetically, but the one she had assumed was Linda turned round and had a good look at her. 'You're not on holiday, are you? I know you. You're the one working at SeaGear.'

Riva nodded, then said yes in an unnaturally loud voice when she realised Linda probably hadn't been able to see the movement of her head. The women started to talk generally about the weather. Riva noticed that there were no men. Later on she understood why.

The chapel was a scene of ordered calm. Bedding had already been organised with one section for the girls, one for the boys, and adults, mostly women, separating the two. A large urn steamed constantly and supplies of tea kept everybody warm. Then she learned where the men were— they were out with the lifeboat, or down at the harbour trying to stem the breach in the wall.

CHAPTER NINE

As soon as the children were put to bed the
women gathered around the tea urn, a single light
bulb shedding an uneven glow over their faces.
Riva could see the anxiety underneath the
enforced cheerfulness as they tried to keep each
other's spirits up.

She did what she could to help out, taking her
turn at washing an unending pile of teacups, but
she felt she stood out like a sore thumb with her
long, sun-bleached hair and bright red and white
skirt tucked into the pair of designer jeans bought
in Kingston just before she flew out. Everybody
else seemed to be wearing the first thing they'd
laid hands on as if fashion was the last thing on
their minds. All except Linda, that was. She was
wearing a tight blue jumper with a low V-neck,
and though she was shod in wellingtons she was
wearing a dressy black pencil skirt and black
nylons. She was vividly pretty, with a broad sense
of humour that kept everybody laughing.

After bustling about finding blankets for some
older women, she flopped down on one of the
hard wooden chapel chairs next to Riva. 'What a
life! Now we sit and bite our fingernails all night!'
She patted her stomach. 'I only hope his dad
doesn't decide to go for a midnight swim!'

A neighbour leaned across. 'When's it due, Linda?'

'I don't know. I haven't kept track. Ages yet.' She laughed comfortably. 'Like his dad—he'll turn up when *he* decides!'

Riva found herself on her feet before she could stop herself. She stood, not knowing where to turn, knowing her face had blanched white at Linda's revelation. She lowered her head and went over to the urn, hiding her face beneath a veil of hair. She felt as if she were about to faint. Then the shock sent a wave of nausea over her. She clenched the edge of the table on which the urn stood and tried not to draw attention to herself. She put a dribble of tea she didn't really want into a cup, then forced herself to return to her chair.

Linda was chatting to some other women about babies. 'How are you getting on with my Richard, then?' she asked bluntly as soon as Riva sat down again.

She held the mug of tea carefully between two hands and with an enormous effort of will forced herself to reply. 'Fine,' she said, in as flippant a tone as she could manage. She knew she would have to try to appear as if nothing was wrong, but it was beyond her to raise her eyes to Linda's just then.

'You can type, he tells me, and speak French. You're a real godsend. He needs somebody like you.'

'It's only temporary. I'm not staying much

longer. I'd only intended to stay a few days in the beginning, then somehow——' she tried to laugh '—you know how it is. You stay longer than you really mean to.'

Linda's brown eyes seemed to widen. 'I thought you were a fixture, more or less, at least?'

'Heavens, no. I'm dying to get back, actually. I've been away far too long.'

'Miss the bright lights, do you?' Linda looked sympathetic. 'You do miss home, I know I did. I couldn't stay away from here for long. Richard was always trying to persuade me to go on foreign postings with him. He told you he was in the Navy, did he?'

Riva nodded. The last thing she wanted was to sit reminiscing about the man she loved with the mother of his unborn child. She felt a wave of nausea sweep over her again. 'I feel a little bit sick. It must be the heat in here.'

Somebody suggested turning down the paraffin stove and one or two others said it was making them feel queasy too. Another cup of tea was pressed into her hand. 'I think I'll go and stand near the door for a minute.' She got up.

With the double doors into the chapel firmly closed so as not to cause a draught to everybody inside, she opened the main door a crack and looked out. Everything looked silver and black, rain-slicked cobbles, pantiled roofs under the street lights. The electricity was on at this top end of the village. The Palmers' end. But down below in what had been the Ravenscroft part the lights were still out. Like them to have a separate source of supply, she thought, trying not to follow through with further black thoughts about the Palmers.

She tried to keep her mind clear and not think of Richard Palmer.

She thought of Isabel and Daniel. Wondered if it was on a night such as this that he had lost his life, leaving Isabel as the Bride of Ravenscroft for sixty years afterwards. She too had been carryng a child on the night Daniel had drowned. In a confusion of similarities she struggled vainly against the feeling she was trapped in a net— Richard and Linda, Linda like Isabel and Richard like Daniel. . .but where did that leave her?

Stifling the horror in the memory of what had happened to Daniel, she went to the wall that bounded the chapel yard. Oblivious to the cold rain driving into her face, she peered out towards the black monster of the sea. Women in centuries past would have stood on this very spot, she realised, praying with tears in their eyes for the safe return of their menfolk.

It wrung her to the soul to feel that even if he did return he would be coming back to the arms of another. The pitiless arch of sky seemed to echo the emptiness in her heart. Turning, she made her way back inside.

Moves were already being made to settle down for the night. 'Who's staying up?' somebody asked.

Another voice said, 'Not you, Linda. You need some sleep.'

'I'll stay up,' volunteered Riva. She could never sleep, knowing Richard was out there risking his life. So long as she knew he was safe she would deal with her private heartbreak in the morning.

The paraffin heater was turned off and blankets issued and, snuggled inside the rough cocoon, she sat up with a couple of other women beside the tea urn. 'Nobody's going to sleep tonight,' one of the women said, looking across at the recumbent forms. The wind still drove like a coach and horses along the twisting village streets.

They talked and dozed and talked some more through the night. Riva rocked back and forth, striving to keep her vigil, her will focused on the one desire, to see Richard, whatever sins he had committed, walk alive and well through the door.

Hours later she felt a hand on her shoulder. 'Can you hear something? I think they're back!' whispered the voice next to her. She sat upright. The wind had died down somewhat, only squalling intermittently in a clatter of rain against the high windows, but underneath that was a sound that was different. There was a movement at the chapel doors.

Suddenly they opened and a couple of men burst through, shedding water off their oilskins as they came. The waiting silence from everyone within was cracked apart.

'They're back!'

Suddenly the entire hall was in uproar. As the

men came through the door, drowsy women were coming to their feet and the commotion brought chidren's heads popping up from their sleeping-bags. One by one the men trooped inside. They all had exhaustion scoured into their faces, hair sea-drenched, skin beaten raw by the salt wind. Riva stayed where she was, eyes searching each face for the one she loved.

'Is everybody back safely?' she heard a voice ask.

A man with a skipper's cap in his hand sat down heavily beside the stove. 'One missing.' He put his head in his hands.

Riva pulled the blanket more tightly around herself. An army of survivors were milling into the hall. She saw Linda step forward, her own eyes searching anxiously among the crowd.

'Where's Dad?' It was Tom. Linda grasped his hand in her own. Riva felt herself get up, the blanket slipping unheeded to the floor. She moved beside them. Then she heard Linda gave a little gasp. She saw her step forward and with a sudden rush throw herself into the arms of a man shouldering his way towards her. It wasn't Richard.

'Thank the lord, Wayne, you're safe! It's let me have you back again!' She clung to him, her arms round his neck, nearly squeezing the life out of him. He was laughing and swung her up in his arms. Riva felt a second jolt to her system. From the way the man held her now there could be no doubt he was her lover. They were rocking together in each other's arms as if never to be parted. Tom slipped his hand out of Linda's and stood anxiously on the edge of the crowd.

'Where's Dad?' He turned to Riva. 'Can you see him?'

Linda and Wayne were still murmuring in each other's arms. With a shock she found herself focusing on a familiar face coming in through the door. It was Ronnie, blond hair plastered to his skull, face strained, looking far older than his seventeen years. He was with another boy of about his own age. A group of older women started to fuss round them, dragging them over to the group round the stove. The urn, she saw, was doing overtime again.

She was about to make her way over to him when she heard Tom go to his mother and shake her by the arm, demanding, 'Where's Dad, Mum?'

Wayne bent down. 'He's all right, son, he's gone down to the quay. Why don't you——?'

'Good. I'll go and fetch him. Come on, Riva.' To her surprise Tom reached for her arm and began to pull her along through the crowd. They let themselves out into the night. As the cold air hit her, Riva felt it had never smelt so sweet.

The two of them hurried down the slope towards the bottom of the high street. The water down here was no higher than it had been earlier in the night. When they got to the level they stood on the edge of the black flood, searching over it for a sign of movement. Suddenly Tom gripped her arm hard. 'There he is!'

She turned to see a torch criss-crossing back and forth from the direction of her cottage.

'Dad, is that you?'

'Sure is.' The dear, dark shape of him looked up beside them. He pulled the boy against him. 'And Riva?' There was a note of surprise in his voice. The torch shone into her face. She put up a hand. Her pain would be evident. She mustn't let him see that. . . The torch snapped off and his other arm came round her shoulders. 'Where did you go to, up to the chapel with the others?'

She nodded, too overwhelmed by the swings her heart had suffered in the last few hours to say anything coherent. The three of them stood huddled together in the darkness with the water lapping round their feet.

'If you want a cup of tea,' said Tom's small voice eventually from lower down, 'you'd better get a move on, Dad.' Riva felt him break away. 'I'll run back up and tell them you're coming. You stay with him, Riva, and make sure he doesn't get lost!'

'I'm lost already,' he murmured, taking her properly into his arms and pressing his lips against the side of her face as soon as Tom had run off up the street. 'You've lost me, Riva. I didn't know what to expect when I stepped out of that boat.'

'I waited for you—I couldn't stop thinking about Isabel and Daniel.' She fought back tears of the relief she felt to hold him at last in her arms again. The brief hours of that other fear, that if the sea didn't claim him Linda would, seemed like a far-off nightmare and of no more consequence. She pulled his head down, sinking into the kiss he gave her like falling into a whirlpool. When she emerged she saw that he was breathless too.

Wrapped in each other's arms, they began to walk back up the street, and when they came to the first street-light they stopped to embrace. 'Palmer's electricity, I suppose?' She looked up at the light, leaning her head on his shoulder. 'That's got another meaning now. You're the most electrifying man I've ever met!' She turned to him, then gave a gasp. 'But, Richard, you've cut yourself!' There was a deep gash across his forehead. She put up her hand and touched it with tenderness in her eyes. Now that she could see him clearly, she saw how worn he looked. 'You poor angel, I'm going to take care of you tonight.'

He kissed her again on the eyes and lightly on the mouth, turning her once more to walk on up the street. 'I could get used to that,' he told her, tightening his grip. 'I could get very used to you taking care of me, Riva.' He looked down at her. His lips compressed into a firm line and he added, 'But we all have our weaknesses, don't we?'

His words and the bitter way in which he uttered them set off a red warning, but concern for him made her ignore it. 'You must be so tired. Let me come back to the Crag,' she suggested on impulse. 'Then I can see to that cut, and maybe. . .' she faltered '. . .maybe I can look after you properly.'

'And see my painting?' He lifted one of her hands to his lips, blue eyes fathomless with meaning.

'Richard. . .' She linked both hands behind his head, striving to make sense of the storming of her emotions. His hours at sea had been the worst of her life and she didn't know how the other women could put up with it as a way of life. Yet she knew she couldn't say this because he would see it as weak and dishonourable. If lives had to be saved every able-bodied man did what he could. Heroism was a way of life, taken for granted, and you put up with it or you got out. She wanted to tell him what it made her feel, how she honoured his courage, but knew the words would embarrass him, so instead she simply stood on tiptoe and raised her lips to his.

'What an insatiable woman you are once your moral qualms have been allayed,' he murmured, covering her mouth roughly with his own before she could say anything. She felt his tongue probe deeply, hungrily into her mouth and his body hardened against her own with the urgency of his response to her kiss. When they moved on he still held her hard against him and she could hear the beating of their hearts in wild tumult to match the storming of the night.

'I'll have to put in a brief appearance here. We won't stay more than five minutes. If you don't want everybody to know what we're about to do you ought to adjust your face. . .' He tilted her chin. 'I thought I was finished for the night, sweetheart, but you could revive a drowned man. Come on. Let's get this over with, then down to business.' Holding her hand, he dragged her up the rest of the slope and into the chapel hall.

His words had puzzled her, sounding harsh, not at all like the loving voice she had heard before. Fatigue, she thought, frowning as she followed him inside; he must be near the limit both emotionally and physically.

The atmosphere was subdued when they went inside. The crew of the trawler whose distress flares had called out the lifeboat were standing around in a silent bunch. One of them was missing. There was no hope for him in a storm like this. There were tears from some of the women, the men's faces stoical, a sense of failure evident in the way they looked at each other.

Richard's own face was grim, and first of all he sought out his kid brother, cuffing him lightly on the shoulder, emotion at the danger they had shared and survived evident in the gesture. Then she saw him go over to Linda, his fingers ruffling protectively through Tom's hair as they all stood talking together in a tight family group.

Linda's man Wayne came up, handing Richard a mug of steaming tea. She felt she would be intruding to go up to them, but Richard turned, his blue eyes piercingly bright as they sought her face in the crowd. Without taking his eyes off her, he swallowed a mouthful of tea, handed the mug to Linda, then bent briefly to say something to his son. He was beside her the next minute.

'OK. Let's punch on down, as Tom would say.' There was a strange edge to his voice. He folded her arm into his and pulled her outside. 'I can think of nothing more perfect than a feather bed with a good woman in it,' he told her with one of his flashing smiles. His eyes were cold.

'Richard——' She was stumbling to keep up with him, but the grip in which he held her hand crooked under his arm made it impossible to slow down. 'I don't——' She bit her lip. 'Maybe you need to have a good sleep. I can always go back to the cottage and. . .' Her voice faltered as he looked coldly into her face.

'Pace getting too hot for you? I thought you wanted to come back and look after me—it was your idea.'

'Yes, but——'

'Maybe you didn't think I'd take you up on it?' He laughed harshly. 'You should know I always accept things at face-value, Riva. No games. Right? You say something—you mean it. That's how it is around these parts. We maybe don't have the subtlety of your London friends, your international jet-set friends—we're simple folk, we always mean what we say.'

'Richard—what do you mean by jet-set friends? What makes you think——'

'Riva,' he reproved. 'I do believe you're trying to talk your way out of it. Surely you won't disappoint a hungry man? I'm hungry for you,

Riva. I need you. And you offered. Now I'm accepting.'

By this time they had reached the gates with the two stone ravens perched on either side. The wind was roaring through the trees, but the rain had stopped now. He drew her up hard against him. 'I can't wait, Riva. I simply can't wait to have you look after me as you said you would. . .' His lips came down, covering her own in a suffocating kiss. She struggled for breath, moving her head from side to side to try to free herself.

His voice was husky and he touched her face with one hand, staring at it in the darkness. 'Come into the house where I can see you properly,' he muttered hoarsely. 'I like to see your face when I kiss you. . .I want to see the desire in your eyes. . .'

He kicked open the unlocked door, both arms around her, and dragged her inside. 'We don't need lights,' he told her. 'Stay in my arms like this and I'll guide you upstairs.' She felt his feverish body envelop her own, half carrying her up stairs that were as familiar to him as his own face. Floorboards creaked as they crossed a landing, then a door swung open into darkness.

She could hear the harsh rasping of his breath, little different from her own as she fought the overwhelming panic at the thought that his love had somehow slipped away. His hands were rough, his lips fierce as they raided her mouth again and again. With lightning speed her clothes were removed and she heard the dull clunk as his boots hit the floor, the slither of his oilskins, the crackle as they flattened under their feet as they swayed together in the darkness.

'Richard, I don't want it to be like this——' she whispered, her skin tingling despite her words as she felt his hand massage her breasts and one knee force her legs apart as he bowed her back on to a bed. His mouth cut off the rest of her words and then she was drowning in a tempest of conflicting emotions as his body spoke to hers of its hunger, herding her doubts ahead of it, driving down deep into her well of love, drawing from her every last sweet gasp of giving she possessed. Her will all gone, he possessed her completely and she willingly handed her heart and soul to him, loving him in every way she knew. Throughout the rest of the night they made love without pause, she answering his slightest demand, and drawing from him, too, the gamut of savage and tender that lived within him.

In too short a time dawn's silver light filled the room. The gale had blown itself out long ago. It was a fair day. He kneeled beside her and she revelled in his naked beauty. He bent over her. 'You're an angel of fire, Riva Hammond. Where am I going to go after this?' He put his face next to hers on the pillow. 'Life goes on, I suppose.'

She thought he meant they had to get up and she rolled over on to her stomach in the tangled sheets, twining her limbs around his, trapping him. 'I want to stay here all day.' She felt him reach over and place a row of kisses down the length of her spine, burying his face against the cushioning flesh.

'You needn't get up just yet. I've got to get in early. I'm going on a sales trip.'

She rolled over. 'You didn't tell me,' she accused.

'You didn't ask.' His eyes swept hers, as soulless as the ocean. 'I mentioned I might,' he amended. 'Come in when you feel like it. I'll bring you coffee and toast now before I leave.'

She sat up, her golden body glowing against the whiteness of the sheets. 'I don't want you to leave just yet. I'm not ready for you to go away.' She reached for his hand. 'You were so wonderful last night, Richard. At first I thought—you seemed different, colder. I suppose I should have made allowances. I was confused at first. I can't imagine what you must have gone through out there in that lifeboat all those hours. It was hell enough just waiting for you.'

'Was it? The women around here live with that. They can cope.'

She felt a hint of criticism in his tone, but before she could say anythng he said, 'You haven't looked above your head.'

She turned. There on the wall was the painting he had mentioned. It was a man of about thirty in a long red robe like Merlin. He was holding out his hand and a young girl with two fair plaits and a velvet green gown was on the point of placing her pale hand in his. The man, the magician, was holding out his other hand indicating a path leading deep into a landscape background, but the girl was looking out of the picture. The moment of decision was evident on her face.

'What is she going to do? Is she going to go with him?' Riva glanced up at Richard.

'I'd like to think so. But no,' he got up off the bed. 'I think they'll go their separate ways, don't you?'

He went out. Riva had another look at the painting. Richard was probably right. But then again. . . She wondered why he seemed to take her innocent question more seriously than she'd intended.

When he returned he was brisk. While she ate her toast he showered in a room across the landing, then returned and donned his dark suit. 'Don't smirk.' Impossibly handsome, with only the small gash on his forehead from the previous night to mar his appearance, he came over to her when he was ready and kissed her lightly on the forehead. 'There are crumbs around your mouth.' With a little jabbing movement of his tongue he licked them away, making it an excuse to bestow a deeper kiss, one that he abruptly cut off. 'Goodbye.' He straightened and for a second stood looking down at her with an expression on his face that made her think of masks. Then he left.

CHAPTER TEN

BY THE time Riva had finished her breakfast, showered and dressed, Richard had been gone an hour. She left the house guessing that Ronnie had also gone on down, marvelling as she went out at the stamina of the two of them after the gruelling hours they had spent at sea the previous night. Sure enough, when she reached the shop Ronnie was busy packing orders in the stockroom. 'I don't know how you do it,' she remarked. She couldn't help but view him in a new light. He made her think of Richard, and her thoughts were tender as she imagined Richard at seventeen.

Later over a cup of coffee they chatted amicably about this and than, and when it got to the point where Ronnie mentioned his mother she lifted her head.

'She died years ago, bless her. Nine, actually,' he told her. 'Naturally Richard was her favourite. He would be, wouldn't he?' He laughed without rancour, events so far away holding no source of bitterness for him.

Riva's swift calculations told her that this would be about the time Richard had got involved with Linda, and she wondered if the two events were connected, and if that was why he understood Ronnie's dive off the straight and narrow so soon after the death of their father. 'I suppose you were your father's favourite?' she asked softly.

'Fair's fair,' he grinned, 'but I was jostling first with Charlotte. She's the one above me.'

'You are lucky, having a large family,' she told him wistfully.

Richard had left some letters to be answered and she started to get on with them. 'Did he mention how long he was going to be?' she asked later as they locked up at the end of the day. It had seemed bleak without him. Already her body was burning with the need for him.

'He was a bit vague. Three days. Maybe more. He didn't seem sure himself.' Ronnie said goodnight. He was staying at the house of a friend nearby.

Riva stared after him as he walked on up the bank. His words had fallen like stones around her ears. Three days? Why hadn't he told her? He had made it sound like a brief absence when he mentioned it this morning, but from what Ronnie said it sounded like an extended selling jag. It was almost as if she had been kept in the dark deliberately.

Surely a trip like this would have had to be planned in advance? He had mentioned some vague idea of going on a sales trip, but as far as she knew nothing definite had been fixed. She'd assumed he would be going out next week perhaps, had even entertained the hope she might go with him if arrangements to run the shop could be made. Now she returned to Sea View with a heavy heart. It seemed she had made too many assumptions.

Next morning there was a spate of phone calls. All women, they each asked to speak to Mr R. Palmer. By now Riva knew the reason.

Turning to the day book as soon as she got in, she had seen the scribbled note Richard had left for her. 'If anybody rings for an interview, fill them in on the details. You know as much as anybody what it entails. Stress that the hours are flexible and I need someone permanent.' One of the callers mentioned that she had read about the job in that morning's Press. Riva went out to get a paper. She scanned it as she walked back.

'Reliable anchorwoman required by small but expanding water-sports business. . .' It went on to give a rough outline of the job and the number to ring. Judging by this morning's response, Richard was going to be spoilt for choice. No doubt, she thought bitterly, when the applicants viewed Richard he would be spoilt too. She felt like tearing the paper into little pieces.

What game was he playing with her? she asked herself furiously. It was rich, coming from somebody who claimed he never played games. If he wanted rid of her why hadn't he said so? His absence now seemed like a flagrant act of cowardice. Didn't he have the courage to tell her to her face he didn't want her around?

But how could he feel this way after what had happened between them the night before last? Surely that meant something? Then she realised that the ad must have gone in earlier. It didn't make her feel any better. The deeper reason for her anger ate silently at her heart until reluctantly she allowed it to surface. Then her feelings threatened to become a fury.

It was obvious he had used her deliberately and callously. He must have known when he took her to bed, when he allowed his body to weave such a sensual spell of apparent love and tenderness over her, that he was about to say goodbye. But why? Didn't his caresses mean anything? Was it all a complete sham? How could such lovemaking stand for nothing? Surely it meant more than the coming together of two bodies in lust, devoid of lasting feeling?

Oh, Richard, she cried in the anguish of her heart, say it isn't true. I can't have misunderstood the sort of man you are. Please say not.

Ronnie had gone out to the post with a bag of parcels and when the phone rang again she picked it up listlessly expecting yet another eager applicant. Then the familiar voice honeyed over the line and she held the receiver hard against her ear as if she could diminish the miles and the misunderstanding that separated them.

But instead of the words of reassurance she longed to hear he was brisk. 'I want some addresses. Can you get that green book from the top drawer of my desk?' he asked without preamble. 'I'm in a call box, so make it snappy, Riva.'

'But, Richard, there's been a spate of girls ringing about my job——' she began.

'The ad's gone in already, has it? I didn't expect it to be go in until tomorrow.'

'But is it true? I'm being replaced?'

'Listen, we can talk about that in a minute. Get the book first, OK?'

Wondering why he hadn't bothered to get enough change for a longer call, she went into the other room, found the book he wanted, and returned with it, crooking the receiver under her chin as she flicked it open.

'Give me the manager's name at Velcron Wet-Gear and Marine Outfitters of Rugby.'

'Are you down there?' She was surprised. He really was making it a trip, as Ronnie had said. She found the addresses and read them over to him.

'Who else is there in that area?' he asked.

'Do you want them?'

'Go on.'

She read them out then added. 'Why didn't you take the book with you?'

'I forgot.'

'Left in too much of a hurry?' Her voice was sharp.

'You might say that. Listen to me, Riva. Arrange all the interviews for next Tuesday. I'll be back then.'

'What about me?'

'What about you?' His voice was guarded.

'Shouldn't I at least receive formal notice of the termination of my employment?' she asked stiffly.

'I wasn't aware we had that sort of agreement. You're casual labour, aren't you? Just passing through.'

The coldness in his tone made her fall silent.

'Listen, Riva, I've got a business to run. What do you expect me to do? Wait until you walk out then run around in circles trying to find somebody to replace you?'

'I'm sure there'll be no end of eager applicants to do for you what I've been doing——' she began acidly.

There was click as the line went dead.

Riva sat for a full minute looking at the traitorous phone. How could it be the bearer of such grief? She ran a hand through her hair, recognising the gesture as one she had picked up from Richard himself. Anger and despair fought a battle and anger struggled to the top. She would not sit here and wallow with a broken heart.

Gathering all her things together, she made her way blindly to the door. Some customers were just coming into the shop and she hustled them outside again. 'I'm sorry, we're closed,' she said to their startled faces. She locked the door firmly, remembering she should have left a note for Ronnie, but felt too distraught to return. Then she walked rapidly away.

Richard Palmer could keep his job, if that was what he thought of her. Did he really think she was simply going to walk out and leave him in the lurch? She ignored the fact that that was what she was doing now. Her head pounded in an irrational tumult.

What did he know about her? Obviously nothing. Lovemaking that should have revealed her inmost soul to him had taught nothing. He was blind. He didn't care a damn. If he cared one jot about her he would understand how she felt when he touched her, when their lips met. . . Anybody who knew her as well as he should know her after taking such intimate liberties with her would know the secrets of her inmost heart. They would know the sort of woman she was and they would know she wasn't what he had suggested before—how had he phrased it? A fair-weather sailor. She was as steadfast as any woman here. Hadn't her vigil through that terrible night of storm and disaster shown him that?

Her anger grew. He could keep his slave labour for somebody else. She was leaving. She was really going now.

Yet when she got into Sea View she crumpled up on the sofa and howled like a baby.

The next morning was Saturday and she decided to stay in bed as long as she could as she wasn't going in to work, but when she got up it wasn't so late after all. She fixed breakfast for herself and sat at the table in the sitting-room window looking out at the now sunlit staithe. It was difficult to believe that the sluggish-looking sea curling over the rocks at the harbour entrance had risen up in such virulent force only two days previously.

She put the radio on, noting that the holiday-makers were out in droves already. Children played on the beach and at the water's edge. The ice-cream kiosk next door to the pub was open and doing brisk business. She prepared to spend a lazy day doing nothing.

She thought of Ronnie at the shop. He would be busy by now. The two girls would be coming in. They would all manage without her. She went to the window again. Maybe she would stroll along soon and let Ronnie know she wasn't coming back. It was only fair. Casual labour she might be, but she wasn't so casual that she would walk out without a word. Besides, she had begun to think of Ronnie as a friend. Hell, she liked him, cared for him in a surprising way that made her think it might be what sisterly feelings were like. He was a sweet, brave boy. Totally without his brother's ruthlessness.

The postman arrived as she was leaving. There was another letter from Dad. After rather a long description of the break he'd taken with Miss Smithson—'to break her into my ways,' he explained—he finished up with news that was welcome. 'Marl's really delighted with the response your lyrics have been getting. He'll be in touch. Expect to see you soon—three-month limit nearly overstepped. What's keeping you?' followed by a series of exclamation marks.

It was the three-month syndrome. Go in, live it

to its limits, then get out. They'd always done that.

Impulsively she threw the letter down on the table and went out. When she reached the shop Ronnie was selling a sailboard to a replica of himself. She didn't interrupt, but looked round for the girls. They were nowhere in evidence.

When he came through grinning from ear to ear at a cash purchase, Riva frowned. 'I can't come in——' she began, but Ronnie broke in at once.

'Am I glad to see you, Riva. The girls have both gone down with summer flu. They made me promise to go and see them later. Trust them to choose a day like today!'

Riva looked gloomily at the sun streaming in through the shop window. 'Oh, but——'

'What's up, darling Riva? Are you missing Richard?'

'Missing him? I wouldn't put it like that. No!' She gave him a cheese smile. 'Oh, well,' she sighed. 'I suppose I'd better roll up my sleeves, hadn't I?' Even as she spoke the shop door opened and a group of customers came in. From then on it was all go until closing time.

'It'll be like this tomorrow,' he told her contentedly as they locked up for the night. 'Aren't we lucky?'

His prediction about trade if not luck was correct, and Monday too dawned bright and hot. She explained to him that she wouldn't be in on Tuesday, and to herself that it would be safe to see Monday out as long as she was well away that evening.

Her determination to get away was as strong as ever. She would drive through the night and reach London at some unearthly hour in the morning, but it wouldn't matter because by then Richard Palmer would belong to another life. The thought of letting their affair linger on until some other girl took her place was too harrowing to contemplate.

Fortunately the shop was busy and she didn't have time to brood over the long letter she would write when she was safely away. Jamaica beckoned and she remembered a travel slogan at the airport. Come back to romance, come back to yourself—come back to Jamaica. Well, she'd had romance, but she would go back to being her old self. Right on.

With thoughts of defiance such as these she was just wrapping some sailing tackle for a customer when an arm brushed against her. With her head bent she hadn't seen anyone approach. 'Sorry——' she began, thinking it was a customer trying to have a closer look at the life-jackets on the rack behind her. Then she gave a gasp.

'Busy?' Richard's blue eyes lazed over hers, as pitiless as an Arctic ocean.

Recovering quickly, she nodded to the busy shop. 'As you see. I hope my replacement can cope.'

'I'll come and give you a hand.'

'Don't bother.'

'My pleasure,' he countered. 'When I heard the weather forecast I guessed the place would be busy.'

'How thoughtful,' she muttered, handing the purchase over to the customer with a mechanical smile.

'Not thoughtful,' he went on in the same intimate tone so only she could hear. 'I couldn't stay away any longer.'

'Why? Things not going too well in the Midlands?'

'On the contrary, they've gone so well that we could shut up shop and live comfortably for the rest of the year on some tropical beach, Riva Hammond. . . Jamaica, for instance.' He eyed her thoughtfully.

'Why don't you do just that, then?' she countered, turning to the next customer.

'I might.'

'Good. I hope you enjoy it.'

She served the customer while Richard was busy showing a selection of safety harnesses to a man with two young sons.

In a brief lull Richard moved beside her. 'I came back to see if you were still here.'

'Why didn't you ring?'

'Sensible. But I've gone beyond the edge where I can think sensibly with regard to you. Why,' he went on in the same rapid undertone, 'have you never mentioned the name Maxwell Hammond?'

'Why should I have?' she started guiltily. 'Is he relevant?'

'Not if you're just passing through, no. But I would have thought it was common courtesy. After all, I told you about *my* marriage.'

'I'm sure I would have done the same in similar circumstances.' She stopped. 'Richard?' A sudden wild thought struck her and she stared at him, round-eyed. 'Richard, tell me something—you don't imagine Maxwell is my husband, do you?'

Richard gave her an encompassing stare. 'Isn't he?'

When she simply stared back in astonishment, he said, 'On the night of the storm, when I got back, I came straight round to the cottage to see if you were all right. . . It was empty of course because you'd gone up to the the chapel with the others. As I flicked my torch around I saw an envelope on the table. I don't know what impulse made me read the name of the addressee on the back.' He shrugged. 'Actually, I suppose I do, if I'm honest. I wanted to fill in a few blanks about you, Riva. Things you were reluctant to tell me yourself.' He paused. 'I can't tell you what turmoil that name aroused. I wanted you to be able to tell me about him of your own accord. It would have shown you wanted to be honest with me. But you didn't say a word. What you did hint, again and again, was that you were just passing through. I thought *he* must be the reason.'

'He was,' she agreed readily. 'But not for the reason you seemed to imagine. He made me footloose because of the way we used to live. But that's *his* way. Not mine. The trouble was, I had to go along with it. You see. . .Maxwell is my *father*.' Her eyes searched his face. 'You still don't know who he is, do you?'

'Should I?'

'Oh, Richard, you are sweet!' A feeling of joy was beginning to bubble up inside her. 'That's the thing I was hiding from you. Not the fact that he was a husband or anything like that! It's that he's *Maxwell Hammond*—the screen writer.' She tilted her head. 'No? You mean to say it *still* means nothing? He'd be most put out!' She laughed, her heart giving a fierce leap at the expression on Richard's face. It made her want to bury herself in his arms. 'Oh, Richard, *please* tell me, is that truly why you were so horrible to me? Did you think I was going to leave. . .because I had a husband in Jamaica?'

Just then another wave of customers surged in. Riva dealt with them as swiftly as possible, impatient for things to be clarified and to know whether her feeling of relief was justified, only just managing to keep on the right side of politeness as two boys took an age to make up their minds over some almost identical T-shirts. She turned as soon as they went out. 'I thought—oh, *no*——' She broke off with a groan as another group of customers came through the door, filling up the shop and demanding immediate attention.

'Let's close the shop when this bunch leave,' murmured Richard as he watched them start to search slowly among the rows of wet suits for the right size, and, while they were trying some on, he told her in a rapid undertone, 'I couldn't believe my eyes when I saw you were still here. I didn't mean to hurt you. I thought I'd give you a fair chance to get out.' And to her startled response he went on, 'I thought you were probably waiting for the right moment, bracing yourself to say goodbye. I felt you would understand why I had to leave so suddenly. Why I had to put the ad in for a replacement. I assumed you'd welcome the chance to make a clean break without any soul-searching.'

'To leave you for *good* just like *that*? After everything that had happened between us?'

'I wouldn't have blamed you. I know what it's like to be passing through. You leave with the good memories intact. No recriminations.'

'Oh, Richard, I love you too much to leave——' She bit her lip. 'I tried to leave once or twice, but some little thing always gave me an excuse to stay. In fact, it wasn't anything little that kept me here at all,' she confessed. 'It was my love for you. And that's . . .that's as deep as the ocean. . .as wide as the sea.'

Half an hour later they made their way up to the top of the cliff, away from all the crowds, and in a sheltered spot Richard spread his jacket on the ground. Down below the sea sparkled, as harmless as a bevy of spangled dancers. He took her hand in his.

'I've been through hell, trying to make up my mind what to do for the best. When you came down to the quayside to meet me off the lifeboat, when I realised you'd stayed up all night with everybody else, I felt such happiness then. At that moment I felt all my worries about your intention to leave fly over the horizon. I told myself it didn't matter a damn about some distant Mr Hammond on the other side of the Atlantic.'

'But shortly after that you seemed so odd, almost as if you wanted to rape me.' She shuddered. 'You dragged me up to the Crag and ripped my clothes away and——' She traced the shape of the veins on the back of one of his hands. 'It was different later. I wouldn't change anything about that night——'

'I'll tell you what it was. It was something Linda told me. She meant it in all innocence. In fact, knowing her as I do, she knew how hard I'd fallen and she was hoping to warn me before I—Riva, you told her you were leaving. She asked me if I knew. You *told* her that?'

Riva blushed. 'I did, it's true. Oh, Richard. It was all a terrible misunderstanding. That night I found out she was pregnant and when she mentioned the father she seemed to be referring to you. At least, that's the conclusion I jumped to. I mean, what was I to think? I went through hell that night, not only in a terror at losing you to the sea, but from fear that even if you did come back it would be back to Linda. Later when Wayne came in I realised who the father really was.'

Richard crumpled her fingers in his and held them to his lips. 'You idiot. But we're both as bad. We seem to have made a habit of getting our lines crossed.'

'I wanted to believe you when you said it was over with Linda—in fact, I did believe you. But when she said something about the father of her child being out with the lifeboat I just jumped to the conclusion she meant you. I felt so awful that I just blurted I was getting out, trying to make light of what I felt for you. I simply couldn't bear the thought of staying. . .'

He lifted her face and began to kiss her mouth with soft, rhythmic kisses. 'You're thoroughly convinced of the truth now, I hope?'

She nodded.

'Linda was delighted when I told her I was getting the divorce sorted out. She's a hopeless case, she simply hadn't got around to doing anything about it. I expect Wayne will eventually persuade her to call at the register office some time.' He looked down at her. 'I did tell you something once, didn't I? Remember the first time we came up here? I said, "Put your hand in mine and I will protect you." I shall, Riva, always and forever. Never doubt me, my love.'

And by the tone of his voice and the way his lips came home to hers, she knew it would always be true.

Later she wrote to her father agreeing that it was brilliant news to find that her songs had been taken up by a well-known singer/heart-throb and she had some more she thought Marl might be able to place. She said she was sorry she wouldn't be coming back yet—Miss Smithson seemed to be doing sterling work—and when she did it would be on a sales trip for a firm called SeaGear, of which she was now a co-director. It was far more enjoyable, she told him, than playing Cinderella.

She also hinted that the trip might be combined with a rather special event. She told him too that she'd ignored his advice about avoiding father-figures, having found the perfect model, but that what was more important was that he was good husband material as well. 'After all,' she said to Richard as she looked up from the letter she was writing in the newly refurbished library at the Crag, 'even though you're still almost under thirty, you've had plenty of practice in both roles—and practice makes perfect, doesn't it, darling?'

The beach was a silver crescent with a line of surf forming and reforming in delicate patterns of lace at its edge. There were two people sitting on white chairs, half in and half out of the water. Riva was almost asleep, senses lulled by the surge and withdrawal of the sea around her ankles. From beneath her straw hat she could see her own legs stretched out in front of her, linked with the ones of her companion, and if she tilted her head as she did every now and then she could bring into view the muscled body beside her. A wave trailed lace over the two pairs of tanned feet, then withdrew.

There was silence apart from the sound of the

surf and the whisper of music from the terrace of the villa. Riva skimmed the bare brown arm next to her own. 'Time for supper, darling,' she sighed.

Richard turned to her. 'It's heaven here, isn't it?' He reached out and took the hand with the gold band on it between his own. 'Heaven where you are. . .Mrs Palmer.'

Mills & Boon

Accept 4 Free Romances and 2 Free gifts

• FROM MILLS & BOON •

An irresistible invitation from Mills & Boon Reader Service. Please accept our offer of 4 free romances, a CUDDLY TEDDY and a special MYSTERY GIFT... Then, if you choose, go on to enjoy 6 more exciting Romances every month for just £1.45 each postage and packaging free. Plus our FREE newsletter with author news, competitions and much more.

Send the coupon below at once to:
Reader Service, FREEPOST, P.O. Box 236,
Croydon, Surrey CR9 9EL

$\times$ — — — — — — **NO STAMP NEEDED** — — —

YES! Please rush me my 4 Free Romances and 2 FREE Gifts! Please also reserve me a Reader Service Subscription so I can look forward to receiving 6 Brand New Romances each month for just £8.70, post and packing free. If I choose not to subscribe I shall write to you within 10 days. I understand I can keep the free books and gifts whatever I decide. I can cancel or suspend my subscription at any time. I am over 18 years of age.

EP86R

Name Mr/Mrs/Miss _____

Address _____

_____

_____ Postcode _____

Signature _____

DON'T MISS OUT ON HOLIDAY ROMANCE!

Four specially selected brand new novels from popular authors in an attractive easy-to-pack presentation case.

THE TIGER'S LAIR
Helen Bianchin

THE GIRL HE LEFT BEHIND
Emma Goldrick

SPELLBINDING
Charlotte Lamb

FORBIDDEN ATTRACTION
Lilian Peake

This year take your own holiday romance with you.

Look out for the special pack from 29th June, 1990 priced £5.40.

DREAM SONG TITLES COMPETITION
HOW TO ENTER

Listed below are 5 incomplete song titles. To enter simply choose the missing word from the selection of words listed and write it on the dotted line provided to complete each song title.

A. . . . . .DREAMS   LOVER

B.   DAY DREAM . . . .   ELECTRIC

C.   DREAM . . . .   CHRISTMAS

D.   . . . . UPON A DREAM   BELIEVER

E.   I'M DREAMING OF A WHITE . . . .   ONCE

When you have completed each of the song titles, fill in the box below, placing the songs in an order ranging from the one you think is the most romantic, through to the one you think is the least romantic.

Use the letter corresponding to the song titles when filling in the five boxes. For example: If you think C. is the most romantic song, place the letter C. in the 1st box.

	1st	2nd	3rd	4th	5th
LETTER OF CHOSEN SONG					

MRS/MISS/MR . . . .

ADDRESS . . . .

. . . .

POSTCODE . . . . .COUNTRY . . . .

CLOSING DATE: 31st DECEMBER, 1990

PLEASE SEND YOUR COMPLETED ENTRY TO EITHER:

Dream Book Offer, Eton House, 18-24 Paradise Road, Richmond, Surrey, ENGLAND TW9 1SR.

OR (Readers in Southern Africa)

Dream Book Offer, IBS Pty Ltd., Private Bag X3010, Randburg 2125, SOUTH AFRICA.

- -